Elevation

Wet Floodproofing

Relocation

Dry Floodproofing

Levees and Floodwalls

Demolition

Homeowner's Guide to Retrofitting

Six Ways To Protect Your House From Flooding

June 1998

Federal Emergency Management Agency

Table of Contents

Chapter 4

Chapter 5

Chapter 6

Chapter 7

Chapter 8

Appendixes

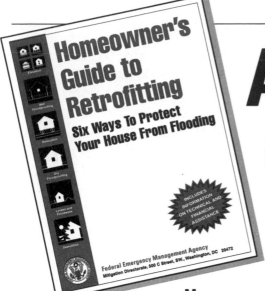

About This Guide

Who This Guide Is For

The Federal Emergency Management Agency (FEMA) prepared this guide specifically for homeowners who want to know how to protect their houses from flooding. As a homeowner, you need clear information about the options available to you and straightforward guidance that will help you make decisions. This guide gives you both, in a form designed for readers who have little or no knowledge about flood protection methods or building construction techniques.

If you are an engineer, an architect, a construction contractor, or someone with skills in those fields, you may want to ask FEMA for copies of technical manuals that cover design and construction in greater detail. For example, all of the flood protection methods described in this guide are described in depth in *Engineering Principles and Practices for Retrofitting Flood Prone Residential Buildings*, FEMA 259, a detailed design manual issued by FEMA in January 1995. If you would like to obtain copies of FEMA 259 or other FEMA documents referred to in this guide, call the FEMA Publications Service Center at 1-800-480-2520. See Appendix A for a list of documents concerning flood protection prepared by FEMA and other agencies and organizations.

How This Guide Can Help You

You should take steps to protect your house if it has been damaged by flooding or is in an area where flooding is likely to occur. But first, you need to know what methods are available, how they work, how much they may cost, and whether they will meet your specific needs. This guide covers all of those issues. It also explains flood hazards and how they can damage your house. Don't forget that flooding is only one of several natural hazards that may threaten your house. This guide includes maps that will help you determine whether your house is in an area where earthquakes or high winds occur, and it explains when your retrofitting project should include protection against these hazards.

DEFINITION

The Federal Emergency Management Agency (FEMA) is the independent Federal agency that administers the National Flood Insurance Program (NFIP). The NFIP is the Federal program, created by Congress in 1968, that makes flood insurance available in communities that adopt and enforce floodplain management ordinances or laws that meet the minimum requirements of the NFIP regulations.

DEFINITION

In this guide, the term **local officials** refers to the employees of your community who are responsible for floodplain management, permitting, building code enforcement, and building inspection. The responsibilities of local officials vary from one community to the next. In your community, you may need to work with one or more of the following: floodplain administrator, building official, city engineer, and planning and zoning administrator.

Your state and local governments probably have adopted building codes and other rules and regulations that you will need to know about. This guide points you in the right direction by explaining how your **local officials** can advise you. Regardless of the flood protection method you choose, <u>you will probably need the help of a construction contractor and a design professional, such as an engineer or architect</u>. This guide describes the types of services you can expect contractors and design professionals to provide.

How To Use This Guide

To get the most from this guide, you should first read Chapters 2, 3, and 4. Chapter 2 explains "retrofitting," and, by describing how flood, wind, and earthquake forces can damage your house, it helps you understand how retrofitting works. Also in Chapter 2 is a discussion of Federal, State, and local financial assistance programs that may help pay for your retrofitting project. Chapter 3 provides short descriptions of the six flood protection methods covered by this guide. It gives you the information you will need as you begin to think about how to protect your house, including the approximate costs, advantages, and disadvantages of each method . Chapter 4 leads you through four steps that will help you decide which method is best for you. Chapter 4 also explains how to work with local officials, contractors, and design professionals.

When you finish Chapter 4, you will be ready to focus on one method. Then you can move to Chapter 5, 6, or 7, depending on your choice. Those chapters describe the methods in greater detail and include photographs and illustrations that show how the methods are applied. Chapter 8 explains how you can protect service equipment (utility systems; heating, cooling, and ventilating systems; and large appliances) in conjunction with the retrofitting method you have chosen.

As you read this guide, you will often find information in the margins of pages — definitions (like the one above), notes, and warnings. Each is identified by a special symbol:

DEFINITION —The meaning of a technical or other special term. Where a term is first used in the text, it is shown in bold type and the definition is provided in the margin. You can also find these and other definitions in Appendix B, *Glossary*.

NOTE —Supplemental information you may find helpful, including things to consider as you plan your retrofitting project, suggestions that can make the retrofitting process easier, and the titles and sources of other publications related to flood protection and retrofitting.

WARNING — <u>Critical</u> information that will help you avoid mistakes that could result in dangerous conditions, violations of your community's ordinances or laws, and possibly delays and higher costs in your retrofitting project. Be sure to read these warnings. If you are unsure about what a specific warning means or what to do to avoid the problem it describes, consult your local officials. Chapter 4 tells you about working with local officials.

A final note before you begin Chapter 2: No guide or other document of this type can anticipate every retrofitting situation or every concern a homeowner may have about undertaking a retrofitting project. If you have questions that this guide does not answer, consult your local officials. They will usually have the information you need. If FEMA has set up a Disaster Field Office (DFO) in your area, in response to a Presidential declaration of a Major Disaster, members of the DFO Mitigation staff can answer questions and advise you. The staff members of the FEMA Regional Office for your state can also help (see Appendix C).

NOTE

Many government agencies, including FEMA, and non-profit organizations, maintain sites on the Internet where you can find information about flooding, high winds, earthquakes, and other hazards. Appendix A includes a partial list of sites that were operating at the time this guide was prepared.

Introduction to Retrofitting

Introduction

Every year, flooding causes over 90 percent of the disaster-related property damage in the United States and accounts for over 75 percent of all Presidential disaster declarations. In fact, over the last decade, property damage related to flooding has averaged well over 3.5 billion dollars a year. In 1996 alone, damages were estimated to have topped 6 billion dollars.

Although recent improvements in construction practices and regulations have made new houses less prone to flood damage, many existing houses continue to be damaged by flooding over and over again. National Flood Insurance Program (NFIP) insurance loss records show that more than 30,000 houses have been flooded more than once during the 6-year period beginning in 1990. These houses, by themselves, have accounted for over 1 billion dollars in flood damages, and their owners feel trapped in a never-ending cycle of flooding and repairing.

The good news is that there are ways that this cycle of repetitive flood damage can be broken. Homeowners across the country have protected their houses from flooding using the techniques described in this guide. One example (Figures 2-1 through 2-3) can be found in the Atlanta area, where some residential neighborhoods built in the 1960's were repeatedly flooded by a nearby stream.

After their house flooded for the second time, one family decided to do something. They hired a contractor, who elevated the house on concrete piers so that it would be above the level of future floods.

Figure 2-1
This house near Atlanta was flooded several times. During the largest flood, the water reached as high as 2 feet above the first floor.

Figure 2-2
The house was elevated in a way that added to both its appearance and its value.

Figure 2-3
Now the house (in the background) is protected from flooding, unlike the flooded house in the foreground.

NOTE

At the outset of the project, the homeowners were concerned about how the house would look after it was elevated. But once construction was complete, the concerns proved groundless. Below the elevated house, traditional latticework was installed in the spaces between the support columns. Access to the front door is now provided by a well-designed double staircase that also serves as an architectural focal point. In addition to providing protection from future floods, elevating the house created a space below that could be used for parking and storage. This retrofitting method worked so well that other property owners in the neighborhood have chosen to protect their houses the same way.

In other areas where flooding has caused repeated damage, entire houses have been moved outside the flood hazard area or protected by floodwalls and levees designed as attractive landscaping features. As you read further in this guide, you will see that it is possible to protect your house from flooding while preserving or even enhancing its attractiveness and value.

Any retrofitting project you undertake must meet the legal requirements of your community, including the floodplain management ordinances your community adopted to participate in the NFIP. By enforcing these ordinances, your community helps reduce future flood damages. As explained later in this chapter, the ordinances are based on the 100-year flood, also referred to as the "base flood." Remember these terms; you will encounter them many times as you read this guide. For further information, see the section *Federal, State, and Local Regulations* on page 20.

NOTE

Retrofitting specifically for earthquake hazards is often referred to as "rehabilitation."

DEFINITION

Hazard mitigation is action taken to reduce or eliminate long-term risk to people and property from hazards such as floods, hurricanes, earthquakes, and fires.

DEFINITION

A **flash flood** is a flood that rises and falls very quickly and usually is characterized by high flow velocities (see page 13). Flash floods often result from intense rainfall over a small area.

What Is "Retrofitting"?

Retrofitting is making changes to an existing building to protect it from flooding or other hazards such as high winds and earthquakes. You have already seen an example of these changes, and you'll learn more in the following chapters. But you may be wondering at this point why retrofitting is necessary. Why aren't houses and other buildings constructed in such a way that they won't need these changes?

One reason is that construction technology, including both methods and materials, continues to improve, as does our knowledge of hazards and their effects on buildings. Many houses existing today were built when little was known about where and how often floods and other hazardous events would occur or how buildings should be protected, and houses being built today may benefit from improvements based on what we learn in the future. As a result, retrofitting has become a necessary and important tool in **hazard mitigation**.

Types of Flooding

This guide focuses primarily on retrofitting for flood protection. If you decide to retrofit your house, you'll need to be aware of other potential hazards as well, such as high winds and earthquakes. They are discussed later, but first it is important that you understand flooding – where and how it occurs, the nature of the threat it poses, and how it can affect your house.

Most of the flooding that occurs in the United States is either riverine or ocean flooding, although flooding also occurs around lakes and ponds and in isolated areas where storm drainage systems are not adequate. Riverine flooding, as its name implies, occurs when rivers and streams overflow their banks (Figure 2-4). Riverine flood waters can move quite rapidly, as in a **flash flood**, or very slowly, as they often do where the land is gently sloping or flat. The primary causes of riverine flooding are rainfall and melting snow (and sometimes a combination of both). Water from rain and melting snow eventually finds its way into stream channels. When the amount of water being carried by a stream exceeds the capacity of the stream channel, it spreads out into the area along the stream, commonly referred to as the floodplain. Usually, the houses and other buildings at greatest risk from riverine flooding are those near the stream channel, where the depths and speed of flood waters are often greatest.

Figure 2-4
This house in Georgia
was inundated by
riverine flooding.

DEFINITION

Storm surge is the rise in the level of the ocean that results from the decrease in atmospheric pressure associated with hurricanes and other storms.

Wave action refers to the characteristics and effects of waves that move inland from an ocean, bay, or other large body of water. Large, fast-moving waves can cause extreme erosion and scour, and their impact on buildings can cause severe damage. During hurricanes and other high-wind events, storm surge and wind increase the destructiveness of waves and cause them to reach higher elevations and penetrate further inland.

Ocean flooding, which is caused by **storm surge** and **wave action**, affects primarily coastal areas, especially those along the beachfront, but it can also affect areas around bays, and it can back up along rivers and streams that empty into bays. Ocean flooding is most dangerous, and causes the most severe damage, where large waves are driven inland by the wind (Figure 2-5). These wind-driven waves occur primarily along the open coast, where they can destroy houses, wash away protective dunes, and erode the soil, often so much that the ground surface is lowered several feet. But they can also move inland where the land is flat and there are no large dunes or other obstacles to break them. In these areas the level of damage can rival that along the open coast.

Figure 2-5
The extreme impact of large, fast-moving waves, combined with the removal of supporting soil by erosion and scour, can have devastating effects on buildings exposed to ocean flooding. This house along the Gulf of Mexico shoreline was destroyed during Hurricane Opal.

DEFINITION

Erosion is the removal of soil that lowers the ground surface across an area. **Scour** is the removal of soil around objects that obstruct flow, such as the foundation walls of houses and other buildings.

DEFINITION

Rainfall **intensity** refers to the amount of rain that falls during a given amount of time. It is usually expressed in inches of rainfall per hour. The higher the number of inches per hour, the greater the intensity.

Ocean flooding can also move inland into low-lying areas beyond the limit of wave action. The danger in these areas is primarily from inundation due to storm surge, but even here, fast-moving flood waters can **scour** away the soil around building foundations.

Another cause of flooding, which can affect houses outside identified floodplains, is the limited capacity of local drainage systems, including storm sewers, culverts, and drainage ditches and swales. These systems are usually designed to carry up to a specific amount of water, which is referred to as the "design capacity" of the system. When heavy rainfall over an area causes the design capacity of the system to be exceeded, water will begin to back up and fill low-lying areas near system inlets and along open ditches. Depending on the amount of rainfall and its **intensity**, the flood water may continue to rise and may eventually affect houses.

A similar problem occurs when drainage system inlets are plugged or obstructed by mud or other debris and when drainage system outlets are covered by water during riverine or coastal floods. In the latter situation, water can flow backwards in the system and reach areas that otherwise might not have flooded.

How Flooding Can Damage Your House

To understand how flooding can damage your house, you need to know about six important flood characteristics: depth/elevation, flow velocity, frequency, rate of rise and rate of fall, duration, and debris load. Most of these characteristics apply to both riverine and ocean flooding, and they can vary – sometimes greatly – from one place to another. The flood conditions at a particular site, such as the location of your house, are determined largely by the combination of these characteristics. The following paragraphs explain these characteristics. The section *Federal, State and Local Regulations*, which you'll find later in this chapter, and Chapter 4 explain how you can find out about the flood conditions at your house.

Depth/Elevation of Flooding

The depth and elevation of flooding are so closely related that they can be viewed as a single characteristic for the purposes of this discussion. Flood depth is the height of the flood water above the surface of the ground or other feature at a specific point. Flood elevation is the height of the flood water above an established reference **datum**. The standard datums used by most Federal agencies and many State and local agencies are the National Geodetic Vertical Datum (NGVD) and the North American Vertical Datum (NAVD); however, other datums are in use. The use of other datums is important because elevations of the ground, flood waters, and other features cannot be meaningfully compared with one another unless they are based on the same datum.

When the elevation of the ground (or another surface such as the **lowest floor** of your house) and the elevation of the flood water are both based on the same datum, the flood depth at any point is equal to the flood elevation at that point minus the elevation of the ground (or other surface) at that point. Figure 2-6 illustrates this relationship. One more thing you should know: ground elevations are established by surveys; flood elevations may be calculated or they may be known from water marks left by past floods.

DEFINITION

An elevation **datum,** or **datum plane**, is an arbitrary surface that serves as a common reference for the elevations of points above or below it. Elevations are expressed in terms of feet, meters, or other units of measure and are identified as negative or positive depending on whether they are above or below the datum plane. Three common elevation datums are Mean Sea Level (MSL), NGVD, and NAVD.

DEFINITION

Under the National Flood Insurance Program, the **lowest floor** of a building is the floor of the lowest enclosed area within the building, including the basement. The only exception is an enclosed area below an elevated building, but only when the enclosed area is used solely for parking, storage, or building access. The elevation of the lowest floor can be very important in retrofitting, as you will see in later chapters.

Figure 2-6
In this example, the 100-year flood elevation is 391.6 feet (10.1 feet above the benchmark elevation of 381.5 feet), and the elevation of the lowest floor of the house is 389.3 feet (7.8 feet above the same benchmark). The flood depth above the lowest floor is therefore equal to 391.6 feet - 389.3 feet, or 2.3 feet during the 100-year flood.

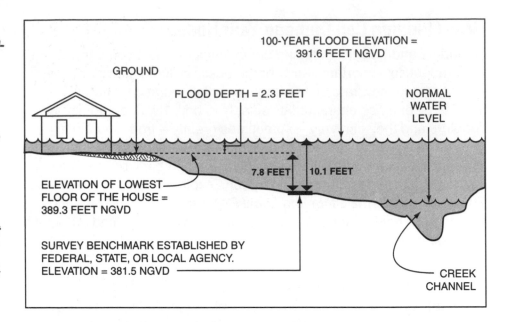

The depth of flooding at your house is important primarily because flood waters, even when they are not moving, exert pressure on structural components such as walls and concrete floor slabs. The pressure exerted by still water is called "hydrostatic pressure." It is caused by the weight of the water, so it increases as the depth of the water increases. As shown in Figure 2-7, flood water, including water that has saturated the soil under the house, pushes in on walls and up on floors. The upward force on floors is called "buoyancy."

As shown in Figure 2-7b, water that has saturated the soil poses a special hazard for basement walls. Because hydrostatic pressure increases with the depth of the water, the pressure on basement walls is greater than the pressure on the walls of the upper floor, as indicated by the arrows in the figure. This pressure is made even greater by the weight of the saturated soil that surrounds the basement.

Figure 2-7
Hydrostatic pressure acts on walls and concrete slab floors. The weight of saturated soils adds to the pressure on basement walls. Figure 2-7a shows a house with a concrete slab floor. Figure 2-7b shows a house with a basement.

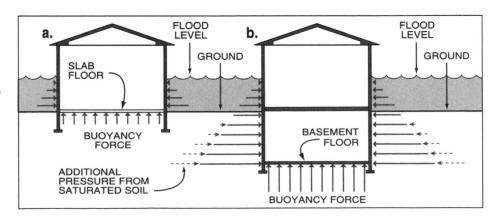

Figure 2-8
The walls of this basement in North Dakota failed because of the pressure exerted by water and saturated soil.

The walls of houses built according to standard construction practice are not designed to resist this pressure. Once the pressure exceeds the strength of the walls (including basement walls), it can push them in (see Figure 2-8), cause extensive structural damage, and possibly cause the house to collapse. In some areas, the buoyant force of hydrostatic pressure on basement floors has pushed entire houses out of the ground.

Note that in the preceding illustration of hydrostatic pressure, no water is shown inside the house. If water is allowed to enter, the hydrostatic pressures on both sides of the walls and floor become the same, or "equalized" (Figure 2-9), and the walls are much less likely to fail. As discussed in Chapters 3, 5, and 6, this is an important consideration in some types of retrofitting methods.

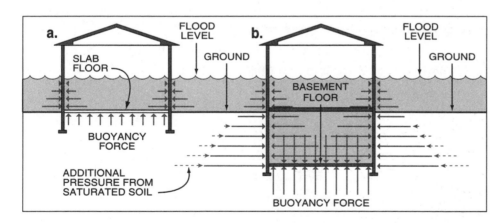

Figure 2-9
Once water enters the house, hydrostatic pressure is equalized. Figure 2-9a shows a house with a concrete slab floor. Figure 2-9b shows a house with a basement.

Flow Velocity

Flow velocity is the speed at which flood waters move. It is usually measured in feet per second, abbreviated as "fps." Flow velocities during riverine floods can easily reach 5 to 10 fps, and in some situations may be even greater. Expressing velocities in fps is common in floodplain studies and engineering analyses. Here, it may be helpful to relate fps to a more familiar unit of measure. For example, 10 fps is roughly equal to 7 miles per hour.

The velocity of riverine flood waters depends on a number of factors; one of the most important is the slope of the stream channel and floodplain. As you might expect, flood waters will generally move much faster along streams in steep mountainous areas than streams in flatter areas. Even within the same floodplain, however, flow velocity can still vary. As water flows over the ground, its velocity depends largely on the roughness of the ground surface. For example, water will flow more swiftly over parking lots, roads, and other paved surfaces and will flow more slowly over ground covered with large rocks, trees, dense vegetation, or other obstacles. Also, flow velocities in the floodplain will usually be higher nearer the stream channel than at the outermost fringes of the floodplain, where water may flow very slowly or not at all. In areas subject to ocean flooding, velocities depend largely on the speed of the wind and, like riverine flow velocities, on the slope and roughness of the ground surface.

If your house is in an area where flood waters are flowing, especially if they are moving more than about 5 fps, the flow velocity is important for several reasons. Flowing water pushes harder on the walls of a building than still water. So instead of just the hydrostatic pressure caused by the weight of the flood water resting against the walls of your house, you have the additional pressure of moving water, referred to as "hydrodynamic pressure" (Figure 2-10). As water flows around your house, it pushes against the side of the house that faces the flow (the upstream side). As it flows past the sides of the house, it creates friction that can tear at wall coverings, such as siding. On the side of the house that faces away from the flow (the downstream side) the water creates a suction that pulls on walls.

Figure 2-10
Moving water acts on the front, sides, and back of a house.

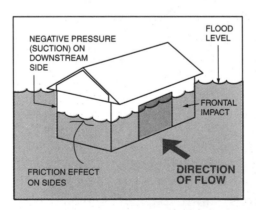

In some situations, the combination of these forces can destroy one or more walls (Figure 2-11), cause the house to shift on its foundation, or even sweep the house away.

Figure 2-11
Moving water can
cause walls to
collapse, as illustrated
by this riverine flood
damage in Georgia.

Flowing water can also cause erosion and scour. As discussed previously, erosion is the removal of soil that lowers the ground surface across an area. Scour is the removal of soil around objects that obstruct flow, such as foundation walls. Both erosion and scour can weaken the structure of a house by removing supporting soil and undermining the foundation. In general, the greater the flow velocity and the larger the house, the greater the extent and depth of erosion and scour. Also, keep in mind that any objects being carried by flood waters will be moving at roughly the same speed as the water. The dangers associated with these objects are discussed later, in the section *Debris Impact.*

Flood Frequency

You may have been told that your house is in the 100-year floodplain, or you may have heard that term used to describe a specific flood. You may also have heard similar terms used, such as 50-year flood or 500-year flood. These terms are occasionally used incorrectly and can be misleading. Flood frequencies are usually determined through statistical and engineering analyses performed by floodplain management agencies and other organizations who need information on which to base engineering designs and flood insurance rates. The results of those analyses define the probability, expressed as a percentage, that a flood of a specific size on a specific stream will be <u>equaled or exceeded</u> in any year.

For example, the flood that has a 1-percent probability (1 in 100) of being equaled or exceeded in any year is referred to as the 100-year flood. This term is simply a convenient way to express probability. It should not be interpreted to mean a flood that happens exactly once every 100 years. Nor does it imply that once a 100-year flood occurs, there is little risk of another 100-year flood occurring in the near future. To the contrary, changes in climatic conditions, such as those caused by El Niño, often result in "clusters" of floods that occur over relatively short times at the same location.

For most homeowners, the value of these terms is that they indicate relative frequencies and sizes. On the average over a long period, a 100-year flood is expected to occur less often than a 50-year flood and more often than a 500-year flood. At the same point along the same flooding source, such as a river, ocean, or bay, a 100-year flood will be more severe than a 50-year flood and less severe than a 500-year flood. For example, if your house is in the 100-year floodplain of a nearby stream or river, the 100-year flood elevation at your house will probably be lower than the 500-year flood elevation, and the water from a 50-year flood might not even reach your house.

The 100-year flood is particularly important for homeowners because it is the basis of NFIP flood insurance rates and regulatory floodplain management requirements. These requirements are discussed in detail on pages 20 and 21. In the NFIP, the 100-year flood is referred to as the "base flood," the 100-year flood elevation as the "base flood elevation" (BFE), and the floodplain associated with the base flood as the Special Flood Hazard Area (SFHA). Other Federal agencies, such as the U. S. Army Corps of Engineers, use the 100-year flood for planning and engineering design, as do many State and local agencies. These agencies often have their own names for the 100-year flood.

Rate of Rise and Rate of Fall

You may not have heard these terms before, but they describe important characteristics of flooding: how rapidly the elevation (and therefore the depth) of water increases and decreases during a flood. These rates are usually expressed in terms of feet or inches per hour. Flood waters with high flow velocities, such as those in areas of steep terrain, and water released by the failure of a dam or levee, usually rise and fall more rapidly than slower-moving floodwaters, such as those in more gently sloping floodplains.

Rate of rise is important because it affects how much warning you will have of an impending flood. For example, homeowners in the floodplains of large rivers like the Mississippi and Missouri may know days in advance that flooding is occurring upstream and will eventually reach their houses. But in the floodplains of streams with high rates of rise, homeowners may have only a few hours' notice of a coming flood or perhaps none at all. With adequate warning, you will be better prepared to take steps to protect yourself and your property. If the flood protection method you choose for your house depends partly on action you must take each time flooding threatens, warning time will be especially important. Chapters 3, 4, 6, and 7 discuss this issue further.

Rate of rise and rate of fall are important also because of their effect on hydrostatic pressure. As explained in the discussion of flood depth/elevation, hydrostatic pressure is most dangerous for a house when the internal and external pressures are not equalized. This situation occurs when the level of water inside the house is significantly higher or lower than the level outside. When flood waters rise rapidly, water may not be able to flow into a house quickly enough for the level in the house to rise as rapidly as the level outside. Conversely, when flood waters fall rapidly, water that has filled a house may not be able to flow out quickly enough, and the level inside will be higher than the level outside. In either situation, the unequalized hydrostatic pressures can cause serious structural damage, possibly to the extent where the house collapses.

Duration

Duration is how long a flood lasts. One of the meanings of duration is how long is takes for the creek, river, bay, or ocean to return to its normal level. As a homeowner, you may be more interested in how long flood waters remain in or around your house or perhaps how long they block nearby streets. In many floodplains, duration is related to rate of rise and rate of fall. Generally, water that rises and falls rapidly will recede more rapidly, and water that rises and falls slowly will recede more slowly. An example of this relationship is the extensive flooding that occurred in the broad, flat floodplains of the Midwest in 1993. In those areas, floodwaters rose slowly and remained high for many weeks or longer.

If your house is flooded, duration is important because it determines how long the structural members (such as the foundation, floor joists, and wall studs), interior finishes (such as drywall and paneling), service equipment (such as furnaces and hot water heaters), and building contents will be affected by flood waters. Long periods of inundation are more likely to cause damage than short periods. Duration can also determine how long your house remains uninhabitable.

Debris Impact

Flood waters can pick up and carry objects of all types – from small to large, from light to heavy – including trees, portions of flood-damaged buildings, automobiles, boats, storage tanks, mobile homes, and even entire houses. In cold climates, wintertime floods can also carry large pieces of ice. Dirt and other substances such as oil, gasoline, sewage, and various chemicals can also be carried by flood waters. All of these types of debris add to the dangers of flooding. Even when flow velocity is relatively low, large objects carried by flood waters can easily damage windows, doors, walls, and, more importantly, critical structural components of your house. As velocity increases, so does the danger of greater damage from debris. If flood waters carrying large amounts of dirt or hazardous substances enter your house, your cleanup costs are likely to be higher and your cleanup time greater.

As you read the remaining sections of this guide, keep these six flood characteristics and their effects in mind. The section titled *Federal, State, and Local Regulations* and Chapter 4 explain how you can find out more about flooding in your area, including flood elevations near your house.

Other Hazards

Two more hazards you should be aware of are high winds (including hurricanes) and earthquakes. For houses in areas subject to these hazards, some retrofitting methods are more appropriate than others. Chapters 3, 4, and 5 discuss this issue further. But regardless of the method you choose, if your house is in a high-wind or earthquake hazard area, your contractor or design professional must ensure that all structural changes made can withstand not only the expected flood forces but the expected forces of winds or earthquakes as well.

Wind is similar to flowing water in that it pushes against the side of the house that faces the wind and pulls on the side that faces away (Figure 2-12). Wind passing over a house can exert a lifting force on the house.

The combination of push, pull, and lift acts on the entire house, including the foundation, and can result in extensive damage if the structural system and **building envelope** are not adequately designed and constructed.

The ability of the wind to damage a building is increased if the wind or windborne debris breach the building envelope by breaking windows, collapsing doors, or puncturing walls. Once the envelope is breached, wind will enter the building and the pressure on the walls and roof will increase, as shown in Figure 2-12. Wind and flood forces can combine in different ways, depending on the directions of the wind and flood flow. When the wind and flood flow direction are the same, the load on

DEFINITION

The **building envelope** is the entire exterior surface of the building — including walls, doors, and windows – which encloses or envelopes the space within.

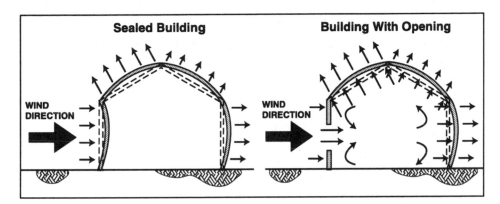

Figure 2-12
Wind forces on sealed building and building with opening.

the house is greater than the load from either wind or flood alone.

The movement of the ground during an earthquake can place large horizontal and vertical loads on a house (Figure 2-13). Like the loads that result from flood flow and wind, earthquake loads can cause extensive damage to a house if they have not been accounted for in the structural design.

High-wind and earthquake hazards vary throughout the United

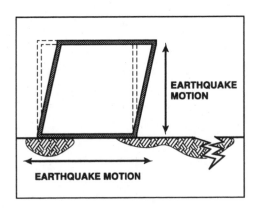

Figure 2-13
Earthquake forces act in both horizontal and vertical directions.

DEFINITION

Under the NFIP, damage to a building, regardless of the cause, is considered **substantial damage** if the cost of restoring the building to its before-damage condition would equal or exceed 50 percent of the market value of the structure before the damage occurred.

Similarly, an improvement of a building (such as reconstruction, rehabilitation, or an addition) is considered a **substantial improvement** if its cost equals or exceeds 50 percent of the market value of the building before the start of construction of the improvement.

For more information, consult your local officials or refer to the FEMA publication *Answers to Questions about Substantially Damaged Buildings,* FEMA 213.

States. In Chapter 4, you will find maps that show the areas where these hazards are greatest.

Federal, State, and Local Regulations

In most communities throughout the United States, construction in floodplains is governed by combinations of Federal, State, and local regulations. At the Federal level, the Federal Emergency Management Agency (FEMA) administers the NFIP. Congress created the NFIP in 1968 when it passed the National Flood Insurance Act. The NFIP is a voluntary program whose goal is to reduce the loss of life and the damage caused by flooding, to help the victims of floods, and to lower the costs of flood damage borne by the taxpayer. It does this by

- guiding future development away from flood hazard areas,

- requiring that new buildings, **substantially improved** buildings, and repaired **substantially damaged** buildings in the SFHA be constructed in compliance with floodplain management ordinances and laws intended to reduce flood damage,

- providing floodplain residents with financial assistance after floods, and

- transferring the cost of flood losses from the taxpayer to the owners of floodprone buildings by requiring the purchase of flood insurance for buildings in the SFHA.

The NFIP operates through a partnership between the Federal Government, the states, and individual communities such as counties and incorporated cities, towns, and villages. Participation in the NFIP is voluntary. In a participating community, affordable federally backed flood insurance is made available to property owners and renters. In return, the community adopts and enforces a floodplain management ordinance or law, which it uses to define a regulatory floodplain and then control development within that floodplain, including new construction, substantial improvement of existing buildings, and repair of substantially damaged buildings.

A participating community's floodplain management ordinance or law must, at a minimum, meet the requirements of the NFIP regulations, but each community is free to establish additional or more stringent requirements as it sees fit. For example, the regulatory floodplain defined by a community must include the entire SFHA, but it may also include other flood hazard areas within the community. Additionally, some states require communities to adopt and enforce floodplain management requirements that exceed the minimum requirements of the NFIP.

These points are particularly important because of their potential effect on your retrofitting project. In this guide, you will find many references to requirements imposed by your community's floodplain management ordinance or law. These are the <u>minimum</u> requirements that all communities must adopt and enforce in their floodplain management ordinances or laws to be compliant with the NFIP regulations. Remember that you must comply with <u>your community's</u> requirements, which may be more stringent.

Usually, communities enforce other requirements that affect construction, both inside and outside of the regulatory floodplain. These requirements include those associated with building codes and land use regulations, such as zoning and subdivision ordinances.

To provide communities with the information they need to enact and enforce floodplain management ordinances or laws, FEMA conducts floodplain studies for communities throughout the United States and publishes the results in *Flood Insurance Studies* (FISs) and *Flood Insurance Rate Maps* (FIRMs) (Figure 2-14). The FIS and FIRM for your community provide information about the names and locations of flooding sources, sizes and frequencies of past floods, limits of the SFHA and **floodway**, flood flow velocities, and elevations of the base flood throughout the SFHA. With this information, communities can manage floodplain development and FEMA's Federal Insurance Administration can establish accurate flood insurance rates.

Other Federal agencies, such as the U. S. Army Corps of Engineers, U. S. Geological Survey, and Natural Resources Conservation Service (formerly U. S. Soil Conservation Service), also publish flood information, as do some State and local agencies. This information is often useful as a supplement to FISs and FIRMs, but because it is developed to meet other needs, it is not used for the NFIP unless it has been reviewed and approved by FEMA.

If you have questions about flood hazards in your community, including the limits of the regulatory floodplain, flood elevations, or sizes and frequencies of past floods, check with your local officials. Usually, they will have copies of the FIS and FIRM for your community. They can also help you determine whether your house is in the regulatory floodplain and advise you about flood protection methods, including those described in this guide. Local officials can also advise you about floodplain management requirements, building codes, and other requirements that may determine the types of changes you can make to your house. See Chapter 4 for more

DEFINITION

The NFIP regulations do not prohibit development in the SFHA. Instead, they require that residential buildings in the SFHA be elevated to or above the BFE. But floodplain development can reduce the amount of space available to convey flood waters and increase flood elevations. So this development must be controlled. The **floodway** is the regulatory means of providing the required control.

The floodway is the portion of the SFHA that must be kept free of new development so that flood elevations will not increase. The floodway usually consists of the stream channel and land along either side. The flood hazard is usually greater in the floodway than in the surrounding areas of the SFHA, referred to as the "flood fringe."

Figure 2-14
This portion of a FIRM shows the SFHA (dark tint), 500-year floodplain (light tint), floodway (hash-marked area between the dashed lines), BFEs (numbered wavy lines and/or numbers in parentheses), and the insurance rate zones (AE and A= SFHA, VE = Coastal High Hazard Area, and X = area outside SFHA).

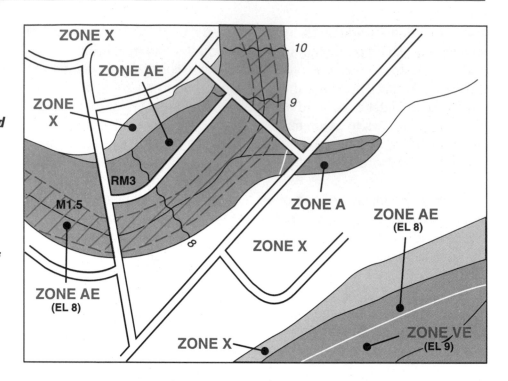

information about working with local officials. You can also get help from your FEMA Regional Office (Appendix C) and the office of your State NFIP Coordinator (Appendix D).

Financial Assistance for Retrofitting

Federal Programs

FEMA and other Federal agencies have a wide array of financial assistance programs that help states, communities, and individual property owners mitigate the negative effects of flood hazards. You may be eligible to receive financial assistance through one or more of these programs that will help pay for your retrofitting project. Check with your local officials, your NFIP State Coordinator (Appendix D), or the FEMA Regional Office for your state (Appendix C).

If a Presidential declaration of a Major Disaster has been issued for your area, you may want to seek information from FEMA and the State and local government representatives supporting the post-disaster recovery of your community. Keep in mind, however, that the funding for these programs is limited and that often not everyone's needs can be met. Also, most of these programs provide grants to State and local governments, who must then set priorities for the use of the grant funds, including any potential use by individual property owners.

Help from FEMA

Increased Cost of Compliance

One of the benefits provided by the NFIP is Increased Cost of Compliance (ICC) coverage. If your house is covered by an NFIP Standard Flood Insurance Policy (SFIP) and has been declared by your community to be substantially damaged by a flood, ICC coverage may help pay for some types of retrofitting. ICC coverage applies to most SFIPs issued or renewed after June 1, 1997.

As noted earlier, your community's floodplain management ordinance or law includes requirements concerning construction in your community's regulatory floodplain. These requirements apply not only to new buildings, but also to existing buildings that have been substantially damaged or that are being substantially improved. If your house falls into one of the latter two categories, you will be required to do one of the following:

- Elevate your house so that its **lowest floor** is at or above the BFE. (See Chapters 3 and 5.)

- Move your house out of the regulatory floodplain. (See Chapters 3 and 7.)

- Wet floodproof the part of your house that is below the BFE. (This alternative is allowed only if the part of your house that is below the BFE is used solely for parking, storage, and building access and is not a **basement** as defined by the NFIP. (See Chapters 3 and 6.)

Remember, communities with more restrictive floodplain management ordinances or laws, may require a greater level of protection.

Although the substantial damage/substantial improvement requirement helps protect lives and property, it has at times placed an additional burden on property owners who were trying to repair their damaged houses. Under the original terms and conditions of the SFIP, the owner of a substantially damaged house was reimbursed for the costs of repairing the damage but not for the costs of complying with State and local requirements concerning substantially damaged structures. For example, the homeowner would not have been reimbursed for the cost of elevating the house, even though elevating was required by State or local ordinances or laws.

In 1997, to provide relief for the owners of houses substantially damaged by flooding, Congress authorized the inclusion of ICC

DEFINITION

Remember, under the NFIP, the lowest floor of a building is the floor of the lowest enclosed area within the building, including the basement. The only exception is an enclosed area below an elevated building, but only when the enclosed area is used solely for parking, storage, or building access.

DEFINITION

The NFIP regulations define a basement as "any area of the building having its floor subgrade on all sides." Note that the NFIP definition of basement does not include what is typically referred to as a "walkout-on-grade" basement, whose floor would be at or above the surface of the ground that touches the outside walls of the building on at least one side (see page 29). This ground surface is referred to as the "adjacent grade."

coverage in the SFIP. With this change in effect, the SFIP reimburses homeowners not only for the cost of repairing flood damage but also for the additional cost, up to a maximum amount stated in the SFIP, of meeting certain State and local floodplain management requirements concerning substantial damage and repetitive losses.

To learn more about ICC coverage, review your SFIP and contact your insurance agent, the FEMA Regional Office that serves your community (Appendix C), or the office of your NFIP State Coordinator (Appendix D). If a Presidential declaration of Major Disaster has been issued for your area, you can get help from the local Disaster Field Office (DFO).

Hazard Mitigation Grant Program

FEMA's Hazard Mitigation Grant Program (HMGP) provides grants to states for their use in conducting mitigation activities following a Presidential declaration of a Major Disaster. HMGP grants are awarded through a cost-sharing arrangement in which the Federal government provides a grant of up to 75 percent of eligible project costs. Therefore, a non-Federal contribution of at least 25 percent is required.

The amount of the total HMGP grant funds available after a Major Disaster is determined by the amount of damage caused by the disaster. A state receives the HMGP grant from FEMA and can then provide some or all of the grant funds to communities. Communities may in turn provide grant funds to individual homeowners for hazard mitigation retrofitting projects (including elevating houses) or use them to acquire badly damaged floodprone houses. HMGP grants may be made only for projects that have been determined to be cost-effective. States and communities often require individual property owners to provide all or part of the non-Federal contribution as a condition of receiving HMGP funds. In these instances, ICC funds (see preceding section) from a flood insurance claim may be applied towards the non-Federal contribution.

Flood Mitigation Assistance Program

FEMA's Flood Mitigation Assistance Program (FMAP) provides grants to states and communities that participate and are in good standing in the NFIP. FMAP grants are awarded annually; their availability is not linked to an area being affected by a disaster or flood. FMAP grants are available for both flood mitigation projects (including elevating floodprone houses and acquiring badly damaged floodprone houses) and the development of state- and community-based flood mitigation plans. Each state and community must have a

FEMA-approved flood hazard mitigation plan in place prior to receiving an FMAP project grant. These plans establish priorities for mitigation projects in the states and communities.

FMAP grants are awarded through a cost-sharing arrangement in which the Federal government provides a grant of up to 75 percent of eligible project costs. Therefore, a non-Federal contribution of at least 25 percent is required. FMAP funds are limited; the annual demand often exceeds the amount available. Also, there are limitations on the amount of grant funds that may be awarded in a given state or community. FMAP grants may only be made for projects that have been determined to be cost-effective.

States and communities often require individual property owners to provide all or part of the non-Federal contribution as a condition of receiving FMAP funds. In these instances, ICC funds from a flood insurance claim may be applied towards the non-Federal contribution.

Help from Other Federal Agencies
Small Business Administration (SBA)

In areas declared a Major Disaster Area by the President, the SBA provides low-interest disaster assistance loans to individuals for both businesses and private residences. These loans cover the cost of rebuilding a damaged building, including the cost of bringing the building into compliance with applicable ordinances and laws. The loans can pay for retrofitting of substantially damaged buildings required by ordinances or laws (including elevating floodprone houses and rebuilding badly damaged floodprone houses at an alternative location), as well as some mitigation projects that are not required by ordinances or laws. At the applicant's request, the amount of the loan may be increased by up to 20 percent for hazard mitigation measures not required by the community's ordinances or laws.

Department of Housing and Urban Development (HUD)

In an area declared a Major Disaster Area by the President, HUD may provide additional, or allow for the reprogramming of existing, Community Development Block Grants. If a community wishes, these grants may be used for retrofitting substantially damaged houses or substandard housing (including elevating floodprone houses and acquiring badly damaged floodprone houses).

U. S. Army Corps of Engineers

The Corps has the statutory authority to participate in flood protection projects that may include residential retrofitting (including elevating

NOTE

This section is not meant to be an all-inclusive description of Federal assistance. Following a Presidentially declared Major Disaster, State and local officials will be briefed on the available types of post-disaster assistance.

floodprone houses and acquiring badly damaged floodprone houses). Contact the appropriate Corps Division office for further information. You can find the address and telephone number in the blue pages (government listings) in your telephone directory.

Natural Resources Conservation Service (NRCS), U. S. Department of Agriculture

The NRCS has the statutory authority to participate in small watershed flood protection projects that may include residential retrofitting. Contact your local Conservationist for further information. You can find the address and telephone number in the blue pages (government listings) in your telephone directory.

Other Assistance Programs

Other Federal programs intended to protect and improve the environmental quality of floodplains may offer financial assistance.

Non-Federal Help
Programs Sponsored by State and Local Governments

States, local governments, and flood control and drainage districts sometimes develop financial assistance programs to promote flood hazard retrofitting projects. Ask your local officials whether such a program exists in your community.

Voluntary Organizations

After floods and other major disasters, voluntary organizations often offer their services to support the rebuilding of houses. Donated materials and labor sometimes become available that could be used to reduce the cost of a retrofitting project. Check with local officials, local service organizations, and houses of worship for information about such services.

Environmental Interest Organizations, Including Land Trusts and Nature Conservancies

Numerous non-government, non-profit, and quasi-public organizations are dedicated to enhancing the environmental benefits of floodplains. Sometimes these organizations provide funds that can be used in the restoration or protection of the natural beneficial value of the floodplain.

An Overview of the Retrofitting Methods

Introduction

This guide describes six retrofitting methods that you should consider as you think about how to protect your house from flooding:

  ELEVATION –Raising your house so that the lowest floor is above the flood level. You can do this in one of four ways.

 WET FLOODPROOFING –Making uninhabited portions of your house resistant to flood damage and allowing water to enter during flooding.

 RELOCATION –Moving your house out of the floodplain to higher ground where it will not be exposed to flooding.

 DRY FLOODPROOFING –Sealing your house to prevent flood waters from entering.

 LEVEES AND FLOODWALLS –Building a floodwall or levee around your house to hold back flood water.

 DEMOLITION–Tearing down your damaged house and either rebuilding properly on the same property or buying or building a house elsewhere.

This chapter describes the six methods in detail. For each method, you will find a section that explains how the method works and where it should and should not be used, lists its advantages and disadvantages, and provides a cost estimate. But first, there are some general cautions about retrofitting that you need to be aware of.

WARNING

In the areas listed below, the hazards to lives and property are usually greater than in other floodprone areas:

- Coastal High Hazard Areas (insurance Zone V, VE, and V1-V30) shown on a Flood Insurance Rate Map (FIRM) (See Figure 2-14.)

- floodways shown on a FIRM (See Figure 2-14.)

- alluvial fan flood hazard areas (Zone AO with depths and velocities) shown on a FIRM

- areas subject to flash floods

- areas subject to ice flows

- areas subject to extremely high-velocity flood flows

Modifying a house to protect it from flood damage in these areas requires extreme care and may also require complex, engineered designs. If your house is in one of these areas, you should consider relocation or demolition (as described later in this chapter and in Chapter 7) rather than any of the other retrofitting methods discussed in this guide. If you have any doubt about whether your house is in an area of unusually severe hazard, consult your local officials.

Cautions

Substantial Damage/Substantial Improvement

As noted in Chapter 2, your community's floodplain management ordinance or law includes restrictions on the types of changes that may be made to a house that has sustained **substantial damage** or that is undergoing **substantial improvement**. These restrictions prohibit or limit the use of some retrofitting measures. Two of the six methods described in this guide – dry floodproofing and levees/floodwalls – may not be used to bring a substantially damaged or substantially improved house into compliance with your community's floodplain management

NOTE

Substantial damage and **substantial improvement** are defined on page 20 and in Appendix B.

ordinance or law. Instead, in accordance, with your community's requirements, you must do one of the following:

- Move the house out of the regulatory floodplain.

- Elevate the house so that its lowest floor is at or above the Base Flood Elevation (BFE).

- Wet floodproof the areas of the house below the BFE and use them only for parking, storage, and building access.

- Demolish the house and either rebuild properly or buy a house elsewhere.

Additional restrictions apply to the use of wet floodproofing. These are described later in this chapter and in Chapter 6.

Another important floodplain management requirement concerns basements. If your house has a basement and your local officials determine that your house is substantially damaged or is being substantially improved, <u>the basement must be eliminated.</u> You can usually do this by filling it with dirt. For floodplain management purposes, the National Flood Insurance Program (NFIP) regulations define a basement as "any area of the building having its floor subgrade on all sides." Your community's floodplain management ordinance or law may include a more restrictive definition of basement.

Note that the NFIP definition of "basement" does not include what is typically referred to as a "**walkout-on-grade**" basement, whose floor would be at or above adjacent grade on at least one side of the building. Depending on your community's floodplain management ordinance or law, the requirement to eliminate the basement in a substantially damaged or substantially improved house may <u>not</u> apply to a walkout-on-grade basement. Instead, you may be able to wet floodproof the basement. However, a wet floodproofed walkout-on-grade basement may be used only for parking, storage, or building access.

Your local officials can tell you more about these restrictions and others that may be specified by local building codes and ordinances (see Chapter 4).

Flood Protection Elevation and Risk

When you retrofit your house, one of the most important things you will do is choose a level of flood protection. In other words, will you protect your house from the base flood, the 500-year flood, or some other flood? In some instances, this decision will be entirely yours; in others, it will depend largely on the regulatory requirements of your community, your state, or both.

DEFINITION

Walkout-on-grade is a term commonly used to describe a basement whose floor is at ground level on at least one side of a house. The term "walkout" is used because most basements of this type have an outside door or doors (entry door, garage door, or both) at ground level (see figure). Note that a basement whose floor is below grade on all sides (a basement as defined by the NFIP regulations) may still have an outside door, but the door will be below ground level and stairs will be required for access.

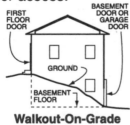

Walkout-On-Grade Basement

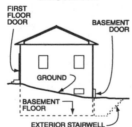

Subgrade Basement

As you will see in this chapter, different retrofitting methods protect your house in different ways. For example, when you elevate your house, you protect it by raising its lowest floor to a specified elevation. In wet floodproofing and dry floodproofing, you use flood-resistant materials, sealants, and shields to protect the part of your house below a specified elevation. When you protect your house with a levee or floodwall, the top of the levee or floodwall must be at a specified elevation. In each of these examples, the specified elevation is referred to as the Flood Protection Elevation (FPE). If flood waters rise above the FPE, your protection is either greatly diminished or eliminated.

If your house has been substantially damaged or is being substantially improved, your community's floodplain management ordinance or law will require an FPE that is at least equal to the BFE (the elevation of the 100-year flood). Communities may require a higher FPE if they wish, or they may be required to do so by State law. Some states and communities require a higher FPE by establishing freeboard requirements, as discussed in the next section. Also, even if substantial damage and substantial improvement provisions do not apply to your house, your community may still enforce regulatory requirements that would affect your choice of an FPE. Your local officials can advise you about this.

Keep in mind that community requirements are usually minimums. Although you cannot use an FPE lower than that required by your community, you are probably free to use a higher FPE if you wish to provide a greater level of flood protection. You may find that your community's floodplain management ordinance or law does not apply to your retrofitting project, in which case you may choose any FPE you wish. In either situation, your choice will be based largely on cost and risk.

In general you will find that the cost of retrofitting increases as your FPE increases. For example, protecting your house to the elevation of the 50-year flood with one of the methods described in this guide will probably cost you less than protecting it to the BFE with the same method. Although using a lower FPE may result in a less expensive retrofitting project, it exposes your house to a greater risk of flood damage. So in choosing an FPE, you must consider not only how much you are willing to pay, but also the level of risk you are willing to accept, including the potential for damage, financial loss, and emotional distress.

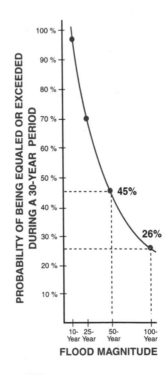

One way to see the relationship between FPE and risk is to look at the probabilities associated with floods of various magnitudes during a period of 30 years, the length of a standard mortgage (see graph at left). The percentages shown along the vertical scale of the graph are the probabilities that a flood will be equaled or exceeded during a 30-year period. As you can see, this probability decreases as the magnitude of the flood increases. So the probability of a flood with an elevation equal to or greater than the FPE you choose decreases as your FPE increases. For example, compare the risks associated with the 50-year flood and the base flood. If you choose an FPE equal to the elevation of the 50-year flood, the probability that a flood as high or higher than your FPE will occur during a 30-year period is 45 percent. But if you choose an FPE equal to the BFE, the probability drops to 26 percent.

Regardless of the FPE you choose or are required to use, you must realize that a larger flood is always possible and that there will always be some risk of damage. If you don't have flood insurance, you should purchase a policy; if you have flood insurance, you should maintain your policy, even if you have protected your house to or above the BFE. Once a house has been retrofitted to meet the NFIP requirements for substantially improved structures, it will probably be eligible for a significantly lower flood insurance rate.

Freeboard

Freeboard is an additional amount of height included in the FPE to provide a factor of safety. If you are protecting your house by elevating it, wet floodproofing it, dry floodproofing it, or building a levee or floodwall, you should include a minimum of 1 foot of freeboard in your FPE, even if your community does not require you to do so. For example, if you are elevating your house to protect it from the base flood, your FPE should be equal to the BFE plus 1 foot.

Freeboard is needed because of uncertainties regarding expected flood elevations. These uncertainties exist for several reasons, but the two primary reasons are limitations of the analytical methods used in floodplain studies and potential effects of future **watershed** development, such as the construction of buildings and roads.

FEMA and all other agencies that perform floodplain studies use a variety of standard engineering methodologies to determine flood frequencies and flood elevations. These methods involve the use of historical data, field measurements, and assumptions and judgments, all of which can affect the accuracy of the results. Some amount of uncertainty regarding the results is therefore unavoidable, and the potential for flood elevations higher than those expected should always be accounted for in retrofitting.

DEFINITION

The **watershed** of a stream is the geographic area that contributes surface water, from rain or melting snow, to that stream.

Development in a watershed can increase the size and frequency of floods in that watershed. In general, watershed development reduces the amount of open ground available to absorb water from rain and melting snow and therefore increases the amount of water that makes its way into streams. As a result, in a developing watershed, an amount of rainfall that might have caused minor floods in the past may cause larger floods, and higher elevations, in the future.

FEMA's floodplain studies are based on the watershed conditions existing at the time the studies are performed. They do not account for potential increases in watershed development or any other changes that might affect the sizes of future floods. The reason for this approach is that one of the primary purposes of Flood Insurance Studies (FISs) and FIRMs is to provide the technical basis for an insurance rate structure. Therefore, the flood hazards must be shown as they are, not as they might be. Also, attempting to predict the level of future watershed development in every study and determine the effects not only would be extremely difficult but also would require additional assumptions and judgments that could increase uncertainty. In many watersheds, however, some amount of development is inevitable. So, providing freeboard is a prudent means of protecting against the increased flood elevations that may result.

DEFINITION

Human intervention is any action that a person must take to enable a flood protection measure to function as intended. This action must be taken every time flooding threatens.

WARNING

Some communities may restrict or prohibit the use of active retrofitting methods for flood protection.

Human Intervention

Retrofitting methods fall into two general categories: those that depend on **human intervention**, which are referred to as "active" methods, and those that do not, which are referred to as "passive" methods. For example, a continuous floodwall around your house does not require human intervention. But what if you have to include an opening for your car? A floodwall with an opening will protect your house only if you can close the opening before flooding occurs. So your floodwall will have to be fitted with a gate (or some other type of closure mechanism), and every time flooding threatens, you will have to be warned far enough in advance that you can close the gate in time.

The need for adequate warning time and human intervention makes active methods less reliable than passive methods. So you should try to avoid active methods when you choose a retrofitting method for your house. If your retrofitting project includes active methods, you must have a plan that describes what actions you will take to make the measures work properly and when you will take those actions.

Other Considerations

Retrofitting methods that are properly designed and applied have several advantages over other types of damage reduction methods. Individual homeowners can undertake retrofitting projects on their own – they do not have to wait for, or depend on, government-sponsored flood control projects. Retrofitting also may be the best means of protection for a homeowner whose house is in an area where a large flood control project, such as a dam, levee, or major waterway improvement, is not feasible, warranted, or appropriate. But you should keep the following in mind whenever you consider a retrofitting project:

• Communities participating in the NFIP require permits for all development within the regulatory floodplain. Under your community's floodplain ordinance or law, any manmade changes to buildings and other structures are considered "development." These changes include improvements and repairs of existing buildings and other structures. Also, communities usually require building permits for many of the activities associated with the retrofitting methods described in this guide. In communities that have adopted a floodplain ordinance or law, health code, and building code, the permits required by these ordinances, laws, and codes may be issued separately or as one combined permit. You may need a permit for the following:

1. Modifying your existing house or building a new house on a flood-free site. Even if your community does not require a building permit, it may require something similar, such as a special permit to regulate floodplain development.

2. Moving a house on public rights-of-way. If you relocate your house, you will probably need such a permit, not only from your community but also from your state and from any other communities and states the house will pass through on its way to the new site.

3. Demolishing a damaged house and restoring the site after demolition, including grading, planting vegetative cover, capping and abandoning utilities, and removing or securing underground septic and fuel storage tanks.

You may wish to obtain the permits necessary for your retrofitting project yourself or arrange for your retrofitting contractor or design professional to obtain them. But remember, you must have the necessary permits in hand before you begin your project. As discussed in Chapter 4, your local officials are the best source of information about State and local permit requirements.

- In addition to meeting the requirements of the NFIP and local codes and floodplain management ordinances, you must comply with the requirements of all other applicable codes, ordinances, and regulations, such as those dealing with building setbacks and wetlands. Again, your local officials are the best source of information about these requirements.

- If your retrofitting project will involve financial assistance from a Federal agency and your property is 50 years old or older, you must work with that agency to ensure that your project complies with the National Historic Preservation Act (16 U.S.C. 470). The act requires that before releasing any Federal assistance, the agency determine whether the property is eligible for inclusion in the National Register of Historic Places and if so, whether your project will have any effect on the property. This requirement may not apply in some emergency situations or if the agency has made prior arrangements with historic preservation officials. For more information, contact your State Historic Preservation Office (Appendix E).

- Most retrofitting measures should be designed and constructed by experienced professionals such as contractors, engineers, and architects. Using professionals helps you make sure that the work is done properly, that code and regulatory requirements are met, and that once completed, the retrofitting measures will work properly.

- Most retrofitting measures cannot be simply installed and forgotten. You will need to periodically inspect and maintain them to be sure that they will continue to work over time, especially if they require human intervention.

- Even though retrofitting will help protect your house from flooding, you should never remain in your house during flooding. Stay informed about flooding conditions by monitoring local radio and television stations. You must be prepared to evacuate when necessary.

- Elevating your house properly may reduce your flood insurance rate. Relocating a house to a site outside the regulatory floodplain eliminates the flood insurance purchase requirement and significantly reduces the cost of flood insurance for an owner who wishes to purchase a policy. Buying flood insurance is strongly recommended, even when it is not required.

Construction Terminology

In the remainder of this guide, you will find many references to common types of house construction, such as frame or masonry, and common types of house foundations, such as slab-on-grade or crawlspace. Even if you are already familiar with these and other house construction terms, take a minute to review the following information before you move to the descriptions of the retrofitting methods.

Construction Type

The most common house construction types are as follows (see Figure 3-1):

frame – walls constructed of wood or light-gage metal studs, with wood, vinyl, or aluminum siding

masonry veneer – frame walls with a non-structural, decorative, exterior layer of brick, stone, or concrete block instead of siding

masonry – walls constructed of brick or concrete block

modular home – frame house assembled on-site from separate sections manufactured elsewhere

manufactured home – prefabricated frame house constructed on a transportable frame

Some houses consist of combinations of two or more of these construction types.

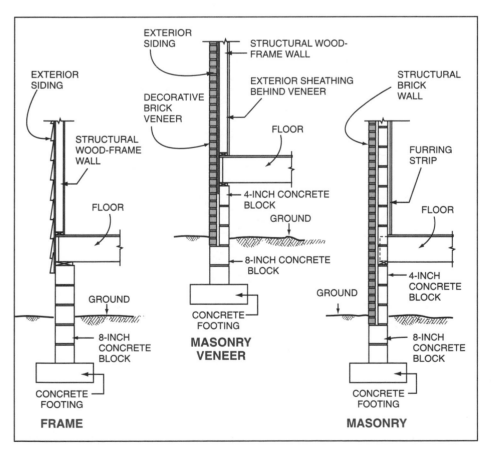

Figure 3-1
Typical cross sections of three common construction types: frame, masonry veneer, and masonry. The foundation shown here for all three construction types consists of concrete blocks and a concrete footing. The same construction types are also found on basement and slab-on-grade foundations (see next section).

DEFINITION

Concrete poured into forms at the construction site is referred to as **cast-in-place**

Foundation Type

Most houses of the construction types listed above are built on the following types of foundations (see Figure 3-2):

basement – with masonry or **cast-in-place** concrete walls

crawlspace – with masonry or cast-in-place concrete walls

slab-on-grade – either (1) a slab with a masonry or concrete foundation or (2) a thickened slab (see Figure 5-5 in Chapter 5)

open foundation – usually concrete or masonry piers, but sometimes wood, concrete, or metal posts, columns, or pilings

Some houses are built on more than one type of foundation. Various combinations of basement, crawlspace, and slab-on-grade foundations are common. Manufactured homes are occasionally installed on basement or crawlspace foundations but are more often supported either by stacks of concrete blocks or by foundation systems designed specifically for manufactured homes.

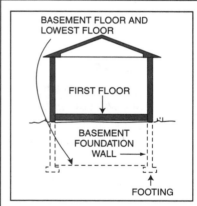

BASEMENT FOUNDATION

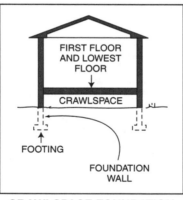

CRAWLSPACE FOUNDATION

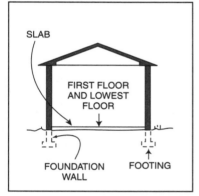

SLAB-ON-GRADE FOUNDATION

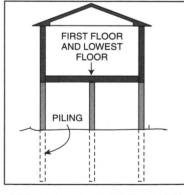

OPEN FOUNDATION (PILINGS)

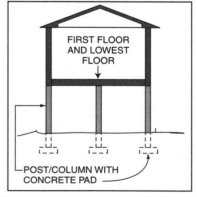

OPEN FOUNDATION (POST/COLUMNS)

Figure 3-2   House foundation types.

Retrofitting Methods and Costs

The following sections describe the retrofitting methods, explain how they work and where they are appropriate, list their advantages and disadvantages, and provide cost estimates. With this information, you will be ready for Chapter 4, *Deciding Which Method Is Right for Your House.*

Elevation (Chapter 5)

Elevating a house to prevent flood waters from reaching living areas is an effective retrofitting method. The goal of the elevation process is to raise the lowest floor to or above the FPE. You can do this by elevating the entire house, including the floor, or by leaving the house in its existing position and constructing a new, elevated floor within the house. The method used depends largely on construction type, foundation type, and flooding conditions.

During the elevation process, most houses (including manufactured homes) are separated from their foundations, raised on hydraulic jacks, and held by temporary supports while a new or extended foundation is constructed below. This method works well for houses originally built on basement, crawlspace, and open foundations. As explained later in this section, the new or extended foundation can consist of either continuous walls or separate piers, posts, columns, or pilings.

A variation of this method is used for houses on slab-on-grade foundations. In these houses, the slab forms both the foundation and the floor of the house. Elevating these houses is easier if the house is left attached to the slab foundation and both are lifted together. After the house and slab are lifted, a new foundation is constructed below the slab.

Alternative techniques are available for masonry houses on slab-on-grade foundations. As described later in this section, these techniques do not require the lifting of the house. Instead, they involve raising the floor within the house or moving the living space to an upper story.

Although elevating a house can help protect it from flood waters, you need to consider other hazards before choosing this method. The walls

WARNING

The cost estimates in this chapter are provided only as guidelines that can help you choose a retrofitting method. They are based on 1998 national averages that may need to be adjusted for local economic conditions. Be sure to get a complete, written cost estimate from your contractor and design professional before you begin any retrofitting project (see Chapter 4).

NOTE

FEMA has produced a videotape entitled *Best Build 3: Protecting a Flood-Prone Home,* which illustrates the retrofitting methods described in this guide (see Appendix A).

DEFINITION

A **footing** is the base of a foundation. Footings are usually made of concrete and may be reinforced with steel bars. Foundation walls are supported on continuous footings; separate foundation members, such as piers, are supported on individual footings.

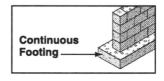

Continuous Footing

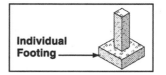

Individual Footing

and roof of an elevated house may be more susceptible to wind forces because they are higher and more exposed. Elevating the house also causes it to become "top heavy" and therefore more susceptible to the overturning forces of earthquakes. In addition, both continuous wall foundations and open foundations can fail as a result of damage caused by erosion and the impact of debris carried by flood waters. If portions of the original foundation, such as the **footings**, are used to support new walls or other foundation members, or a new second story, they must be capable of safely carrying the additional loads imposed by the new construction and the expected flood, wind, and earthquake forces.

Elevating on Continuous Foundation Walls

This method is normally used in flood hazard areas where the risks of wave action and high-velocity flow are low. After the house is raised, the existing foundation is often saved and the existing foundation walls are extended. The new portions of the walls are usually made of masonry block or cast-in-place concrete. Although it may seem to be the easiest way to elevate a house, this method may involve some complications.

Depending on the size of your house, the amount of elevation, and the magnitude of the potential environmental loads (such as those from floods, wind, earthquakes, and snow), your contractor may have to modify or reinforce the footings and foundation walls to ensure the structural stability of the house. The original footings may have to be replaced with larger footings. It may also be necessary to reinforce both the footings and the foundation walls with steel bars.

As explained in Chapter 2, unequalized hydrostatic pressure exerted by flood waters can collapse walls regardless of the construction materials used. If flood waters are expected to be more than about a foot deep, openings must be installed in the foundation walls so that water can flow into and out of any enclosed area below the newly elevated house. When the water levels on both sides of the foundation walls are the same, the hydrostatic pressure is equalized. If you are elevating your house in connection with repairs of substantial damage or as part of a substantial improvement, your community's floodplain management ordinance or law will require that you install openings in all areas below the BFE.

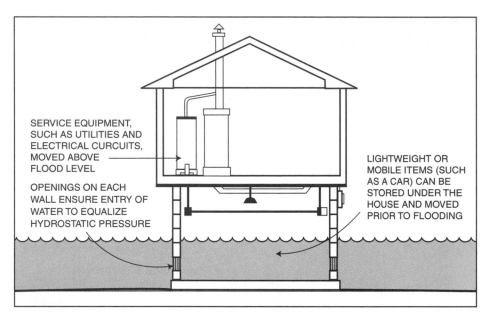

SERVICE EQUIPMENT, SUCH AS UTILITIES AND ELECTRICAL CURCUITS, MOVED ABOVE FLOOD LEVEL

OPENINGS ON EACH WALL ENSURE ENTRY OF WATER TO EQUALIZE HYDROSTATIC PRESSURE

LIGHTWEIGHT OR MOBILE ITEMS (SUCH AS A CAR) CAN BE STORED UNDER THE HOUSE AND MOVED PRIOR TO FLOODING

Figure 3-3
Typical cross-section of house elevated on continuous foundation walls.

Figure 3-4
Retrofitted house elevated on extended continuous foundation walls.

WARNING

If you elevate a house that has been substantially damaged or is being substantially improved, your community's floodplain management ordinance or law will not allow you to have a basement, as defined under the NFIP. The NFIP regulations define a basement as "any area of the building having its floor subgrade on all sides." If your house has such a basement, you will be required to fill it in as part of any elevation project. Note that the NFIP definition of basement does not include what is typically referred to as a "walkout-on-grade" basement, whose floor would be at or above the adjacent grade on at least one side.

Elevating on Open Foundations

Unlike continuous foundations, open foundations consist of individual vertical structural members that support the house only at key points. Because they present less of an obstacle to flood flows than continuous walls, open foundations can be used where the risks of wave action and high-velocity flood flow are greater. Most open foundations consist of piers, posts, columns, or pilings.

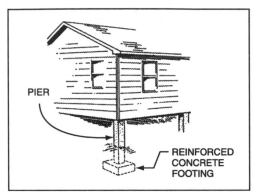

House elevated on piers.

Piers. The most common type of open foundation is a pier foundation. Piers are built with masonry block or are made of cast-in-place concrete. The bottom of each pier sits on a concrete footing. Pier foundations are used in conventional construction; they are not just a means of elevating a floodprone house. In conventional use, they are designed primarily for vertical loading – to hold the weight of the house. They are not normally designed to resist large horizontal forces – such as those associated with moving flood water, waves, impacts from floodborne debris, wind, and earthquakes. As a result, pier foundations are generally used where the risks of wave action and high-velocity flow are low to moderate and the potential for earthquakes is low.

If you decide to elevate your house on a pier foundation, you should expect your contractor to reinforce the piers and footings with steel rods and to tie the piers to the footings so they will not separate under flood or other forces. Adequate connections between the piers and the house are also necessary so that the house and foundation will resist lateral loads from flood, wind, and earthquake and uplift from buoyancy.

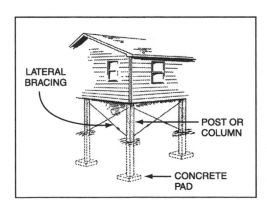

House elevated on posts or columns.

Posts or columns. Posts (also referred to as columns) are usually made of wood or steel. They are generally square but may also be round. Posts and columns are set in holes, and their ends are encased in concrete, or supported on concrete pads (as in the figure). After posts or columns are set, the holes are filled with concrete, dirt, gravel, or crushed stone. Unlike piers, which are designed to act as independent supports, posts and columns usually must be connected to each other with bracing. The bracing may consist of wood, steel rods, or guy wires. The type you choose is usually determined by cost, flood conditions, expected loads, the availability of materials, and local construction practice. Like piers, posts and columns are generally used where the risks of wave action and high-velocity flow are low to moderate.

House elevated on pilings.

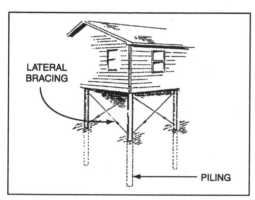

Pilings. Pilings are usually made of wood, but steel and **precast concrete** are also common in some areas. Pilings are similar to posts, but instead of being set in holes, they are driven into the ground or **jetted** in with high-pressure streams of water. Also, pilings are embedded deeper in the ground than either piers or posts. As a result, piling foundations are less susceptible to the effects of high-velocity flow, waves, debris impact, erosion, and scour than the other types of open foundations. Pilings differ from piers and posts also in that they do not rest on footings. Instead they are driven until they rest on a solid support layer, such as bedrock, or until they are embedded deep enough that the friction between the ground and the pilings will enable them to resist the loads that are expected to act on them.

Because driving and jetting pilings requires bulky, heavy construction machinery, an existing house must normally be moved off its existing foundation and set on **cribbing** until the operation is complete. As a result, elevating a house by placing it on a piling foundation will usually require more space and cost more than elevating with another type of foundation. Piling foundations are used primarily in areas where other elevation methods are not feasible, such as where flood waters are deep and the risks of wave action and high-velocity flow are great. For example, piling foundations are used extensively in oceanfront areas exposed to high-velocity flow, waves, and high winds.

DEFINITION

Concrete materials such as posts, beams, and blocks that are brought to the construction site in finished form are referred to as **pre-cast.**

DEFINITION

Jetting is a process in which the hole for the installation of a piling is made by a high-pressure stream water from a nozzle attached to the bottom of the piling.

DEFINITION

Cribbing usually consists of a framework of criss-crossed timbers that provides temporary structural support.

Figure 3-5
This coastal house in Florida was elevated on pilings so that it would be less vulnerable to damage from coastal flooding.

Elevating by Extending the Walls of the House or Moving the Living Space to an Upper Floor

For masonry houses on slab-on-grade foundations, two alternative elevation methods are available. One is to remove the roof, extend the walls of the house upward, replace the roof, and build a new, elevated floor at the FPE. This technique works best where the floor needs to be raised less than 4 feet to reach the FPE. The elevated floor can be either a new slab or a new wood-framed floor. For a new slab, fill dirt is placed on top of the old slab and the new slab is built on top. If a new wood-framed floor is built, the area between it and the old slab is left open and becomes a crawlspace.

The second technique is to abandon the entire lower floor, or lower enclosed area, of the house and move the living space to an existing or newly constructed upper story. This technique works best for multi-story houses where the FPE is more than 4 feet above the level of the lower floor. The abandoned lower floor or enclosed area is then used only for parking, storage, or building access.

These techniques, like the others, have their limitations. The portions of the house below the FPE will be exposed to flooding and must therefore be made of flood-resistant materials. That is why this method is generally applicable only to masonry houses. A frame house would be much more easily damaged by flooding. The area below the FPE cannot be used for living space; it may be used only for parking, storage, or building access. In addition, all appliances and utilities must be moved to the upper floor. Also, openings must be cut into the walls of the lower floor to allow water to enter during flooding so that the hydrostatic pressure on the walls will be equalized. In essence, the lower floor is wet floodproofed (see the next section for a discussion of wet floodproofing).

Figure 3-6
The owner of this floodprone house in south Florida decided to build a new frame second story on top of his masonry first story. The new second story is well above the BFE.

ADVANTAGES AND DISADVANTAGES OF ELEVATION

Table 3.1

ADVANTAGES	DISADVANTAGES
• **Elevation to or above the BFE allows a substantially damaged or substantially improved house to be brought into compliance with your community's floodplain management ordinance or law.**	• Cost may be prohibitive.
• Elevation reduces the flood risk to the house and its contents.	• The appearance of the house may be adversely affected.
• Except where a lower floor is used for storage, elevation eliminates the need to move vulnerable contents to areas above the water level during flooding.	• Access to the house may be adversely affected.
	• The house must not be occupied during a flood.
	• Unless special measures are taken, elevation is not appropriate in areas with high-velocity flows, waves, fast-moving ice or debris flow, or erosion.
• Elevation often reduces flood insurance premiums.	
• Elevation techniques are well-known, and qualified contractors are often readily available.	• Additional costs are likely if the house must be brought into compliance with current code requirements for plumbing, electrical, and energy systems.
• Elevation does not require the additional land that may be needed for the construction of floodwalls or levees.	• Potential wind and earthquake loads must be considered.
• Elevation reduces the physical, financial, and emotional strain that accompanies floods.	

NOTE

As discussed under Financial Assistance for Retrofitting in Chapter 2, the cost of elevating a substantially damaged house may be an eligible flood insurance claim under Increased Cost of Compliance (ICC) coverage.

Adding a new second story to a single-story house may require that the foundation be strengthened so that it can support the additional load. You must consult an engineer if you plan to use this method. The second story can be frame or masonry (to match the lower floor). The method you choose will depend on the advice of your engineer, cost, appearance, the availability of materials and experienced contractors, and the risks of other natural hazards such as hurricanes and earthquakes.

Approximate Costs

The costs shown in Table 3.2 are for elevating frame and masonry houses a total of 2 feet. The costs for extending utilities and adding or extending staircases are included. The costs shown for elevating frame and masonry houses on existing slab-on-grade foundations are based on the assumption that the house is raised with the existing slab attached.

COST OF ELEVATING A HOUSE 2 FEET

Table 3.2

CONSTRUCTION TYPE	EXISTING FOUNDATION	RETROFIT	COST (per square foot of house footprint)
FRAME (For frame house with brick veneer on walls, add 10 percent)	Basement or Crawlspace	Elevate 2 Feet on Continuous Foundation Walls or Open Foundation	$17
	Slab-on-Grade	Elevate 2 Feet on Continuous Foundation Walls or Open Foundation[1]	$47[1]
MASONRY	Slab-on-Grade	Elevate 2 Feet on Continuous Foundation Walls or Open Foundation	$47[1]
	Basement, Crawlspace, or Slab-on-Grade	Extend Existing Walls 2 Feet and Create New Elevated Living Area	$35

[1] Price shown is for raising the house with the slab attached.

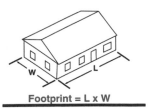

DEFINITION

The **footprint** of a house is the land area it covers (see figure). This area is equal to the length of the house multiplied by its width. Note that the footprint is not equal to the total square footage of all the floors in the house.

Footprint = L x W

You can estimate the cost of elevating more than 2 feet by adding $0.75 per square foot of house **footprint** for each additional foot of elevation up to 8 feet. For elevations greater than 8 feet, add $1.00 per square foot for each additional foot of elevation.

Occasionally, slab-on-grade houses are raised without the slab. Although this method can be less expensive than raising the house with the slab, it involves detaching the house from the slab and requires extensive

NOTE

See Chapter 6 for a discussion of **flood-resistant materials.**

alterations to interior and exterior walls. As a result, raising the house without the slab is usually done only when the house has been severely damaged by a flood, fire, or other catastrophe.

The cost of abandoning an existing lower level will depend on whether the house already has an upper level that can be used for living space. If an upper level is available, abandoning the lower floor would involve primarily elevating or relocating utilities, adding openings in the lower-level walls, and ensuring that all construction materials are **flood-resistant**. The cost would be approximately $5 - $10 per square foot of building footprint. This method is well-suited to a house with a walkout-on-grade basement, which can be wet floodproofed and used for parking, storage, or building access. Adding a new frame upper level and raising the roof to accommodate the new level would cost approximately $40 - $50 per square foot depending upon the amount of interior finishing.

SAMPLE COST ESTIMATE

It may be helpful to consider an example in which a 40-foot by 25-foot frame house with brick veneer walls is elevated a total of 4 feet on continuous foundation walls.

Footprint= 40 feet x 25 feet = 1,000 square feet

Cost of elevating 2 feet =
$17 per square foot of footprint = **$17,000**

Cost of elevating 2 additional feet =
2 x $0.75 per square foot of footprint = **$1,500**

Total = $18,500 + 10% for brick veneer =
$18,500 + $1,850 = $20,350 or
$20.35 per square foot of house footprint

WARNING

If your house has been substantially damaged or is being substantially improved, your community's floodplain management ordinance or law will <u>restrict</u> your use of wet floodproofing to attached garages and enclosed areas below the BFE that are used solely for parking, storage, or building access. For more information, consult your local officials or refer to FEMA's Technical Bulletin 7-93, *Wet Floodproofing Requirements for Structures Located in Special Flood Hazard Areas.*

NOTE

See Chapter 6 for a discussion of **flood-resistant materials.**

Wet Floodproofing (Chapter 6)

Wet floodproofing a house is modifying the uninhabited portions of the house (such as a crawlspace or an unfinished basement) so that flood waters will enter but not cause significant damage to either the house or its contents. The purpose of allowing water into portions of the house is to ensure that the interior and exterior hydrostatic pressures will be equal. Allowing these pressures to equalize greatly reduces the likelihood of wall failures and structural damage. Wet floodproofing is often used when all other retrofitting methods are either too costly or are not feasible. But it is practical in only a limited number of situations.

Because wet floodproofing allows flood waters to enter the house, all construction and finishing materials below the FPE must be resistant to flood damage. For this reason, wet floodproofing is practical only for portions of a house that are not used for living space, such as a basement as defined by the NFIP regulations, a walkout-on-grade basement, crawlspace, or attached garage. It would not be practical for most slab-on-grade houses, in which the living space is at or very near the ground level. Whether or not wet floodproofing is appropriate for your house will depend on the flood conditions, the FPE you have selected, the design and construction of your house, and whether your house has been substantially damaged or is being substantially improved.

If you are considering wet floodproofing, keep the following in mind:

- Your house should have space above the FPE in which you can temporarily store items that could be damaged by flood waters.

- If your furnace, water heater, or other service equipment is below the FPE, it must be protected as well. You may be able to do this by moving the equipment to another floor, elevating it, or protecting it in place. (An example of protection in place is surrounding a furnace with an interior floodwall -- see Chapter 8).

- Any construction and finishing materials below the FPE that are not **flood-resistant** must be removed or replaced with materials that are flood-resistant.

- If a flood occurs, you will not be able to live in your house as long as flood waters remain inside.

- Wet floodproofing does nothing to alleviate the threat of damage from high-velocity flood flow and wave action.

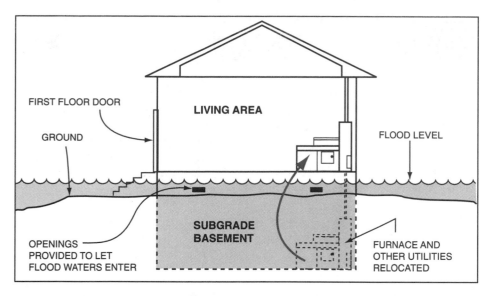

Figure 3-7   *A house with a wet floodproofed subgrade basement. (If this house were substantially damaged or substantially improved, the basement would have to be filled in; see the Warning at right.)*

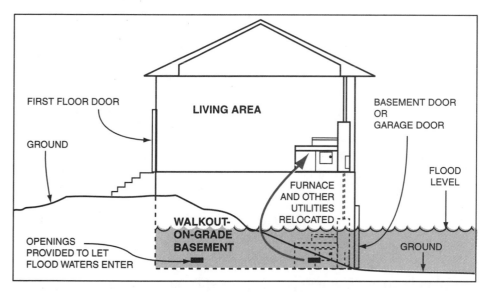

Figure 3-8   *A house with a wet floodproofed walkout-on-grade basement.*

WARNING

If you wet floodproof a house that has been substantially damaged or is being substantially improved, your community's floodplain management ordinance or law will <u>not</u> allow you to have a basement, as defined under the NFIP. The NFIP regulations define a basement as "any area of the building having its floor subgrade on all sides." If your house has such a basement, you will be required to fill it in as part of any wet floodproofing project. Note that the NFIP definition of basement does not include what is typically referred to as a "walkout-on-grade" basement, whose floor would be at or above grade on at least one side.

Table 3.3 ADVANTAGES AND DISADVANTAGES OF WET FLOODPROOFING

WARNING

After flood waters recede from the area around a house with a wet floodproofed basement, the homeowner will usually want to pump out the water that filled the basement during the flood. But if the soil surrounding the basement walls and below the basement floor is still saturated with water, removing the water in the basement too quickly can be dangerous. As the water level in the basement drops, the outside pressure on the basement walls and floor becomes greater than the inside pressure (see figure). As a result, the walls can collapse and the floor can be pushed up or cracked.

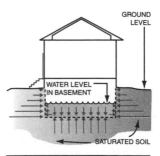

ADVANTAGES	DISADVANTAGES
• No matter how small the effort, wet floodproofing can, in many instances, reduce flood damage to a house and its contents.	• **Wet floodproofing may be used to bring a substantially damaged or substantially improved house into compliance with your community's floodplain management ordinance or law only if the areas of the house below the BFE are used solely for parking, storage, or building access.**
• Because wet floodproofing allows internal and external hydrostatic pressures to equalize, the loads on walls and floors will be less than in a dry floodproofed house (discussed later in this section).	• Preparing the house and its contents for an impending flood requires human intervention and adequate warning time.
• Costs for moving or storing contents (except basement contents) after a flood warning is issued are covered by flood insurance in some circumstances.	• The house will get wet inside and possibly be contaminated by sewage, chemicals, and other materials borne by flood waters. Extensive cleanup may be necessary.
• Wet floodproofing measures are often less costly than other types of retrofitting.	• The house must not be occupied during a flood, and it may be uninhabitable for some time afterward.
• Wet floodproofing does not require the additional land that may be needed for floodwalls and levees (discussed later in this section).	• It will be necessary to limit the uses of the floodable area of the house.
• The appearance of the house is usually not adversely affected.	• Periodic maintenance may be required.
• Wet floodproofing reduces the physical, financial, and emotional strain that accompanies floods.	• Pumping flood waters out of a wet floodproofed basement too soon after a flood may lead to structural damage (see the Warning at left).
	• Wet floodproofing does nothing to minimize the potential damage from high-velocity flood flow and wave action.

DEFINITION

The **lowest adjacent grade (LAG)** is the lowest ground surface that touches any of the exterior walls of your house.

Wet floodproofing is generally less expensive than the other flood protection methods described in this guide. Table 3.4 shows approximate costs per square foot of building footprint for wet floodproofing houses on basement and crawlspace foundations to heights of 2, 4, and 8 feet. In a house with a basement, this height is measured from the basement floor (but see warning on page 47). In a house with a crawlspace, this height is measured from the **lowest grade adjacent to the house**. The costs shown include those for adding wall openings for the entry and exit of flood waters, installing pumps, rearranging or relocating utility systems, moving large appliances, and making it easier to clean up after flood waters recede. The costs shown for basements in Table 3.4 are valid only for unfinished basements. Wet floodproofing a finished basement would require that all non-flood-resistant finishing materials be permanently removed or replaced with flood-resistant materials. As a result, wet floodproofing costs for finished basements would be higher than those shown below and would vary depending on the amount of finishing to be removed or replaced.

COST OF WET FLOODPROOFING

Table 3.4

CONSTRUCTION TYPE	HEIGHT OF WET FLOODPROOFING (in feet above basement floor or LAG[1])	EXISTING FOUNDATION	COST (per square foot of house footprint)
FRAME OR MASONRY	2	Basement[2]	$1.70
		Crawlspace	$1.30
	4	Basement[2]	$3.50
		Crawlspace	$3.25
	8	Basement[2]	$10.00
		Crawlspace	NA[3]

[1] House with basement: feet above basement floor; house with crawlspace: feet above LAG
[2] Unfinished
[3] A house would almost never have a crawlspace 8 feet high, which is nearly the height of a full story.

SAMPLE COST ESTIMATE

It may be helpful to consider an example in which a 40-foot by 25-foot house on a crawlspace foundation is wet floodproofed to a height of 4 feet above grade.

Footprint= 40 feet x 25 feet = 1,000 square feet

**Total cost of wet floodproofing 4 feet =
$3.25 per square foot of house footprint = $3,250**

Relocation (Chapter 7)

Moving your house to high ground, outside the flood hazard area, is the most effective of the retrofitting methods described in this guide. Retrofitting literature commonly refers to this method as relocation. When space permits, you may even be able to move your house to another location on the same piece of property.

Relocating a house usually involves jacking it up and placing it on a wheeled vehicle, which delivers it to the new site. The original foundation cannot be moved, so it is demolished and a new foundation is built at the new site. The house is installed on the new foundation and all utility lines are connected. Relocation is particularly appropriate in areas where the flood hazard is severe, such as where flood conditions are characterized by one or more of the following:

- deep water
- short warning time
- high flow velocity
- long duration
- high rates of rise and fall
- wave action
- high debris potential

Relocation is also appropriate for homeowners who want to be free of worries about damage from future floods that may exceed a selected FPE.

Although similar to elevation, relocation requires additional steps that usually make it more expensive. These include moving the house, buying and preparing a new site (including building the new foundation and providing the necessary utilities), and restoring the old site (including demolishing the old foundation and properly capping and abandoning old utility lines).

Houses of all sizes and types can be relocated, either as a unit or in segments. One-story frame houses are usually the easiest to move, particularly if they are built on a crawlspace or basement foundation that provides easy access to the floor framing. Masonry houses can also be moved, but usually with more difficulty and at a higher cost.

Professional house movers can advise you about the things you need to consider in deciding whether to relocate. The structural soundness of your house will have to be checked. Also, you may need to find a place where you can store furniture and other belongings temporarily. In most instances, however, the contents of your home may remain in the house

OVERVIEW OF THE RETROFITTING METHODS

while it is being moved. And keep in mind that there must be a clear route to the new site. Narrow roads, restrictive overpasses, and bridges with low weight limits may make it impossible for your house to be moved to the new site. Also, many states and communities have requirements that govern the transport of houses and other buildings on public rights-of-way.

ADVANTAGES AND DISADVANTAGES OF RELOCATION

Table 3.5

ADVANTAGES	DISADVANTAGES
• **Relocation allows a substantially damaged or substantially improved house to be brought into compliance with your community's floodplain management ordinance or law.** • Relocation significantly reduces flood risk to the house and its contents. • Relocation can either eliminate the need to purchase flood insurance or reduce the amount of the premium. • Relocation techniques are well-known, and qualified contractors are often readily available. • Relocation reduces the physical, financial, and emotional strain that accompanies flood events.	• Cost may be prohibitive. • A new site (preferably outside the flood hazard area) must be located and purchased. • The floodprone lot on which the house was located must be sold or otherwise disposed of. • Additional costs are likely if the house must be brought into compliance with current code requirements for plumbing, electrical, and energy systems.

The Table 3.6 shows approximate costs per square foot of house footprint for relocating houses of different types. The costs include those for moving the house, building a new foundation at the new site, installing the house on the new foundation, and hooking up all utilities. The costs shown are based on the assumption that the house will be moved less than 5 miles and installed on the same type of foundation as it originally had.

HOMEOWNER'S GUIDE TO RETROFITTING

COST OF RELOCATING

Table 3.6

WARNING

The relocation costs shown here are for a 1,000-square-foot house. Because relocation costs do not increase proportionally with the size of a house, the cost per square foot of moving a larger house may be less than that shown here.

CONSTRUCTION TYPE	EXISTING FOUNDATION	COST (per square foot of house **footprint**)
FRAME (For frame house with brick veneer on walls, add 10 percent)	Basement	$32
	Crawlspace	$27
	Slab-on-Grade	$51
MASONRY	Basement	$49
	Crawlspace	$32
	Slab-on-Grade	$61

The costs shown in Table 3.6 do not include the cost of restoring the old site, which would be approximately $12 per square foot of building footprint regardless of construction type or foundation type. Also not included is the cost of any new property that must be purchased.

NOTE

As discussed in Financial Assistance for Retrofitting in Chapter 2, the cost of relocating a substantially damaged house may be an eligible flood insurance claim under ICC coverage.

SAMPLE COST ESTIMATE

It may be helpful to consider an example in which a 40-foot by 25-foot frame house with masonry veneer on a basement foundation is relocated to a site less than 5 miles away and installed on the same type of foundation.

Footprint= 40 feet x 25 feet = 1,000 square feet

Cost of relocating=
$32 per square foot of footprint = **$32,000**

Additional cost for masonry veneer =
$32,000 x 10% = **$3,200**

Additional cost for site restoration =
$12 per square foot of footprint = **$12,000**

Total cost of relocation =
$47,200 or
$47.20 per square foot of house footprint

Dry Floodproofing (Chapter 7)

In some situations, a house can be made watertight below the FPE, so that flood waters cannot enter. This method is called "dry floodproofing." Making the house watertight requires sealing the walls with waterproof coatings, impermeable membranes, or supplemental layers of masonry or concrete. Also, doors, windows, and other openings below the FPE must be equipped with permanent or removable shields, and backflow valves must be installed in sewer lines and drains. The flood characteristics that affect the success of dry floodproofing are flood depth, flood duration, flow velocity, and the potential for wave action and floodborne debris.

Flood depth is important because of the hydrostatic pressure that flood waters exert on walls and floors. Because water is prevented from entering a dry floodproofed house, the exterior pressure on walls and floors is not counteracted as it is in a wet floodproofed house (see the discussion on pages 12 and 13). The ability of house walls to withstand the pressure exerted by flood waters depends partly on how the walls are constructed. Typical masonry and masonry veneer walls, without reinforcement, can usually withstand the pressure exerted by water up to about 3 feet deep. When flood depths exceed 3 feet, unreinforced masonry and masonry veneer walls are much more likely to crack or collapse. An advantage of masonry and masonry veneer walls is that their exterior surfaces are resistant to damage by moisture and can be made watertight relatively easily with sealants. In contrast, typical frame walls are likely to fail at lower flood depths, are more difficult to make watertight, and are more vulnerable to damage from moisture. As a result, wet floodproofing is not recommended for houses with frame walls.

WARNING

Dry floodproofing may <u>not</u> be used to bring a substantially damaged or substantially improved house into compliance with your community's floodplain management ordinance or law.

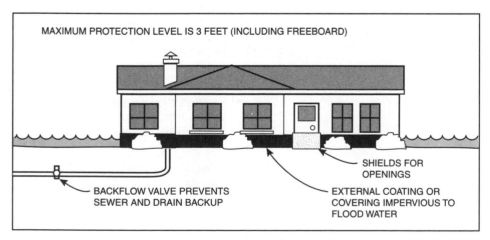

Figure 3-9
A typical dry floodproofed house.

ADVANTAGES AND DISADVANTAGES OF DRY FLOODPROOFING

Table 3.7

WARNING

Because dry flood-proofing requires human intervention, you must be willing and able to install all flood shields and carry out all other activities required for the successful operation of the dry floodproofing system. As a result, not only must you be physically capable of carrying out these activities, you must be home or able to go home in time to do so before flood waters arrive.

ADVANTAGES	DISADVANTAGES
• Dry floodproofing reduces the flood risk to the house and its contents.	• **Dry floodproofing may not be used to bring a substantially damaged or substantially improved house into compliance with your community's floodplain management ordinance or law.**
• Dry floodproofing may be less costly than other retrofitting methods.	• Ongoing maintenance is required.
• Dry floodproofing does not require the additional land that may be needed for levees and floodwalls (discussed later in this chapter).	• Flood insurance premiums are not reduced for residential structures.
• Dry floodproofing reduces the physical, financial, and emotional strain that accompanies floods.	• Installing temporary protective measures, such as flood shields, requires human intervention and adequate warning time.
	• If the protective measures fail or the FPE is exceeded, the effect on the house will be the same as if there were no protection at all.
	• If design loads are exceeded, walls may collapse, floors may buckle, and the house may even float, potentially resulting in more damage than if the house were allowed to flood.
	• The house must not be occupied during a flood.
	• Flood shields may not be aesthetically pleasing.
	• Damage to the exterior of the house and other property may not be reduced.
	• Shields and sealants may leak, which could result to damage to the house and its contents.
	• Dry floodproofing does nothing to minimize the potential damage from high-velocity flood flow and wave action.

Even if masonry or masonry veneer walls are reinforced to withstand the pressure of deeper water, the effects of buoyancy must be considered. The buoyancy force exerted by water greater than 3 feet deep is often great enough to crack a slab floor or push it up. For this reason, dry floodproofing usually is not appropriate method of protecting a house from flooding over 3 feet deep.

Duration of flooding is critical because most sealing systems will begin to allow some amount of seepage after prolonged periods of exposure to water. If your house is in an area where flood waters remain high for days, you should use a different retrofitting method. Areas with a risk of high-velocity flood flow, wave action, or both are not appropriate locations for dry floodproofing. Either condition may render dry floodproofing totally ineffective and cause severe damage.

Dry floodproofing is not recommended for houses with basements. Saturated soils pressing against basement walls can damage them or cause them to fail. The buoyancy force exerted by saturated soils below the basement can cause the basement floor to fail or even push the entire house up.

Sealant systems, especially those that rely on membranes and coatings, can be punctured by ice and other types of debris. If your house is in an area where flood waters are known to carry debris, you should select a different retrofitting method.

The Table 3.8 shows approximate costs for individual components that make up a dry floodproofing system.

WARNING

Even concrete block and brick walls should <u>not</u> be dry floodproofed above a height of 3 feet, unless an engineering analysis has been performed which shows that the walls will withstand the expected hydrostatic and hydrodynamic loads and debris impact forces. The effects of buoyancy on slab floors must also be considered.

COST OF DRY FLOODPROOFING

Table 3.8

COMPONENT	COST	PER
Sprayed-on Cement (above grade)[1]	$3.30	Square Foot of Wall Area Covered
Asphalt (two coats on foundation below grade)[1, 2]	$1.10	Square Foot of Wall Area Covered
Waterproof Membrane (above grade)[1]	$1.10	Square Foot of Wall Area Covered
Drainage Line Around Perimeter of House	$31	Linear Foot
Plumbing Check Valve	$620	Lump Sum
Sump and Sump Pump (with backup battery)	$1,000	Lump Sum
Metal Flood Shield	$73	Square Foot of Shield Surface
Wood Flood Shield	$23	Square Foot of Shield Surface

[1]Cement, asphalt, and membrane are alternative sealant methods.
[2]Does not include the cost of excavation

As you can see from the table, the total cost for dry floodproofing a house will depend largely on the size of the house, FPE, types of sealant and shield materials used, number of plumbing lines that have to be protected by check valves, and number of openings that have to be covered by shields.

SAMPLE COST ESTIMATE

It may be helpful to consider an example in which a 40-foot by 25-foot masonry house on a slab-on-grade foundation is dry floodproofed to a height of 2 feet above the lowest floor. The house is assumed to have two doors below the FPE and to require three plumbing check valves and one sump pump.

Perimeter of house = 40 feet + 25 feet + 40 feet + 25 feet = 130 feet
Protected wall area = 130 feet x 2 feet high = 260 square feet
Cost of waterproof membrane = $1.10 x 260 square feet = **$286.00**

Width of doors to be protected = 3 feet per door x 2 = 6 feet
Protected door area = 6 feet x 2 feet high = 12 square feet
Cost of wood door shields = $23 x 12 square feet = **$276.00**

Cost of perimeter drainage line = 130 feet x $31 per square foot = $4,030
Cost of three plumbing check valves = $620.00 x 3 = **$1,860**
Cost of one sump pump = **$1,000**

Total cost of dry floodproofing =
    $7,452.00 or
    $7.45 per square foot of house footprint

Levees and Floodwalls (Chapter 7)

Levees and floodwalls are types of flood protection barriers. A levee is typically a compacted earthen structure; a floodwall is an engineered structure usually built of concrete, masonry, or a combination of both. When these barriers are built to protect a house, they are usually referred to as "residential," "individual," or "on-site" levees and floodwalls. The practical heights of these levees and floodwalls are usually limited to 6 feet and 4 feet, respectively. These limits are the result of the following considerations:

- As the height of a levee or floodwall increases, so does the depth of water that can build up behind it. Greater depths result in greater water pressures, so taller levees and floodwalls must be designed and constructed to withstand the increased pressures. Meeting this need for additional strength greatly increases the cost of the levee or floodwall, usually beyond what an individual homeowner can afford.

- Because taller levees and floodwalls must be stronger, they must also be more massive, so they usually require more space than is likely to be available on an individual lot. This is especially true of levees.

WARNING

Levees and floodwalls may not be used to bring a substantially damaged or substantially improved house into compliance with your community's floodplain management ordinance or law.

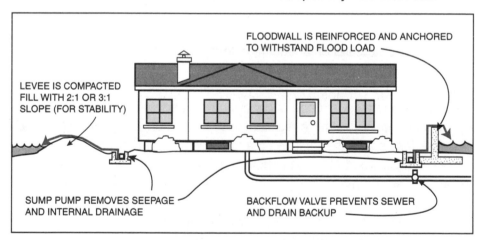

FLOODWALL IS REINFORCED AND ANCHORED TO WITHSTAND FLOOD LOAD

LEVEE IS COMPACTED FILL WITH 2:1 OR 3:1 SLOPE (FOR STABILITY)

SUMP PUMP REMOVES SEEPAGE AND INTERNAL DRAINAGE

BACKFLOW VALVE PREVENTS SEWER AND DRAIN BACKUP

Figure 3-10 House protected by levee (left) and floodwall (right).

Both levees and floodwalls should provide at least 1 foot of **freeboard**. For example, if you are building a levee to protect your house from the base flood, the top of the levee should be 1 foot above the BFE.

For a levee to be effective over time, it must be constructed of soils that cannot be easily penetrated by flood waters, it must have proper side slopes for stability, and it must be periodically inspected and maintained. In areas where high flow velocities could erode the surface of a levee, the side of the levee exposed to flood water is usually protected with a

NOTE

Freeboard is explained on page 31.

covering of rock, referred to as riprap, or with other erosion-resistant material. Levees can surround a house, or they may be built only across low areas and tied into existing high ground.

Figure 3-11
House protected by levee, which holds back the flood waters shown in the lower half of the photograph. Note that the levee ties in to high ground created by the road embankment.

WARNING

Special design considerations are necessary when levees or floodwalls are built to protect a house with a basement. Even though the surface water is kept from coming into contact with the house, the soil below the levee or floodwall and around the house can become saturated, especially during floods of long duration. The resulting pressure on basement walls and floors can cause them to crack buckle, or even collapse (see page 133).

A floodwall can surround a house, or, depending on flood depths, site topography, and design preferences, it can protect isolated openings such as doors, windows, and basement entrances, including entry doors and garage doors in walkout-on-grade basements. When built with decorative bricks or blocks or as part of garden areas, floodwalls can become attractive architectural or landscaping features. But they can also be built solely for utility, usually at a much lower cost.

Because a floodwall is made of concrete or masonry rather than compacted earth, it is more resistant to erosion than a levee and generally requires less space than a levee that provides the same level of protection. But floodwalls are usually more expensive. As a result, floodwalls are normally considered only for sites where there is not enough room for a levee or where high flow velocities may erode a levee. Also, some homeowners prefer floodwalls because they can be more aesthetically pleasing and allow for the preservation of existing site features, such as trees.

As shown in Figure 3-10, an interior drainage system, including a sump pump, must be installed in the area protected by a levee or floodwall. The purpose of the system is to remove rainwater trapped inside the protected area and, during flooding, to remove water that enters through seepage or infiltration. It also may be necessary to include an opening in a levee or floodwall that will provide access for a car or other vehicle. All openings must be equipped with closures similar to those used in dry floodproofing.

ADVANTAGES AND DISADVANTAGES OF
LEVEES AND FLOODWALLS

Table 3.9

ADVANTAGES	DISADVANTAGES
• The house and the area around it will be protected from inundation, and no significant changes to the house will be required. • Flood waters cannot reach the house or other structures in the protected area and therefore will not cause damage through inundation, hydrodynamic pressure, erosion, scour, or debris impact. • The house can be occupied during construction of levees and floodwalls. • Levees and floodwalls reduce the flood risk to the house and its contents. • Levees and floodwalls reduce the physical, financial, and emotional strain that accompanies flood events.	• **Levees and floodwalls may not be used to bring a substantially damaged or substantially improved house into compliance with your community's floodplain management ordinance or law.** • Cost may be prohibitive. • Periodic maintenance is required. • Human intervention and adequate warning time are required to close any openings in a levee or floodwall. • If a levee or floodwall fails or is overtopped by flood waters, the effect on the house will be the same as if there were no protection at all. • An interior drainage system must be provided. • Local drainage can be affected, possibly creating or worsening flood problems for others. • The house must not be occupied during a flood. • Access to the house may be restricted. • Levees and floodwalls do not reduce flood insurance rates. • Floodplain management requirements may make levees and floodwalls violations of codes and/or regulations. • A large area may be required for construction, especially for levees. • Hydrostatic pressure on below-ground portions of a house may still be a problem, so levees and floodwalls are not good retrofitting methods for houses with basements.

Figure 3-12
House protected by a
floodwall designed as
a landscaping feature.

The following tables show approximate costs for levees and floodwalls of various heights and for additional levee and floodwall components that may be needed.

COSTS OF LEVEES AND FLOODWALLS

Table 3.10

COMPONENT	COST (per linear foot)
Levee – 2 feet above ground	$37
Levee – 4 feet above ground	$69
Levee – 6 feet above ground	$115
Floodwall – 2 feet above ground	$85
Floodwall – 4 feet above ground	$124

COSTS OF ADDITIONAL LEVEE AND FLOODWALL COMPONENTS

Table 3.11

COMPONENT	COST	PER
Levee Riprap	$31	Cubic Yard
Interior Drainage System	$4,200	Lump Sum
Closure (each)	$73	Square Foot of Closure Area
Seeding of disturbed areas	$0.05	Square foot of Ground Area

SAMPLE COST ESTIMATE

It may be helpful to consider two examples, in which a 40-foot by 25-foot house with a walkout-on-grade basement is protected by a 4-foot-high levee or a floodwall of the same height. In these examples, the floodwall/levee encloses an area at the walkout-on-grade level at the back of the house, ties into existing high ground on the sides of the house, and contains one opening that can be used for pedestrian or vehicle access (see figures).

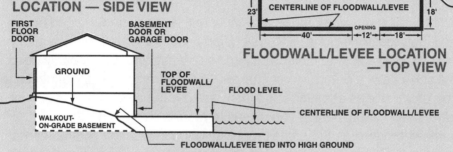

FLOODWALL/LEVEE LOCATION — SIDE VIEW

FLOODWALL/LEVEE LOCATION — TOP VIEW

Levee:
Length of levee = 99 feet (not including opening)

Construction cost = $69 per linear foot x 99 feet = **$6,831**
Cost of interior drainage system = **$4,200** (lump sum)

Size of opening = 4 feet high by 12 feet wide = 48 square feet
Cost of closure = 48 square feet x $73 per square foot = **$3,504**

Area of levee face requiring riprap =99 feet x 10.8 feet = 1,069 square feet

Riprap required (assuming thickness of 1 foot) = 1,069 cubic feet = 40 cubic yards
Cost of riprap = $31 per cubic yard x
    40 cubic yards = **$1,240**

Area of property to be reseeded is assumed to be top of levee (5 feet), face of levee on house side (12.6 feet), and a 5-foot-wide strip on each side of levee. Total width = 27.6 feet. Total area to be reseeded = 99 feet (length of levee) x 27.6 feet = 2,732 square feet.
Cost of reseeding = 2,732 square feet x $0.05 per square foot = **$137**

Total Cost of Levee = $15,912 or approximately $143 per linear foot (including closure)

Floodwall:
Length of floodwall is same as length of levee = 99 feet
Construction cost = $124 per linear foot x 99 feet = **$12,276**
Cost of interior drainage system = **$4,200** (lump sum)
Cost of closure is same as for levee = **$3,504**
Cost of reseeding is same as for levee = **$137**

Total Cost of Floodwall = $20,117 or approximately $181 per linear foot (including closure)

NOTE

The costs for levee construction can vary greatly depending on the distance between the construction site and the source of the fill dirt used to build the levee. The greater the distance that fill dirt must be hauled, the greater the cost.

With a height of 4 feet and a slope of 2.5:1 the face of the levee on the water side would span 10.8 feet

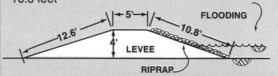

CROSS-SECTION SHOWING DIMENSIONS OF A 4-FOOT-HIGH LEVEE

Demolition (Chapter 7)

Demolition, as a retrofitting method, is tearing down a damaged house and either rebuilding properly somewhere on the same property or moving to a house on other property, outside the regulatory floodplain. This retrofitting method may be the most practical of all those described in this guide when a house has sustained extensive damage, especially severe structural damage.

Whether you rebuild or move, you must tear down your damaged house and then restore the site. Site restoration usually involves filling in a basement, grading, and landscaping. As a result, you will probably need the services of a demolition contractor. The contractor will disconnect and cap all utility lines at the site and then raze the house with a bulldozer or other heavy equipment. If you decide to rebuild on the old site or somewhere else on the same property, your construction contractor may be able to do the demolition and site restoration work as part of the house construction.

Remember, all demolition, construction, and site restoration work must be done according to the regulatory requirements of your community. Permits may be required for all or part of this work. If you decide to rebuild on the site of your old house, you must rebuild properly, which means ensuring that the lowest floor of your new house is at or above the FPE. You can do this by elevating your new house on an extended foundation as described in the *Elevation* section in this chapter or on compacted fill dirt. If your property includes an alternative building site outside the regulatory floodplain, a better approach is to build on that site, where you can use standard construction practices, including the construction of a basement. Remember, if you rebuild on the existing site, within the regulatory floodplain, your community's floodplain management ordinance or law will not allow your new house to have a basement (as defined by the NFIP regulations).

The advantages and disadvantages of demolition vary depending on which of the following three options you choose:

1. rebuilding on the existing site

2. rebuilding on an alternative, flood-free site elsewhere on your existing property

3. moving to a house on other property, outside the regulatory floodplain

The advantages and disadvantages of option 1 are same as those listed in Table 3.1 for the elevation method (see page 43). The advantages and disadvantages of options 2 and 3 are the same as those listed in Table 3.5 for the relocation method (see page 51), with the following exceptions: If you choose option 2, you will avoid the need to buy new property and dispose of your existing property.

If you decide to demolish your damaged house and rebuild somewhere on your existing property (option 1 or 2 above), your costs will be those for tearing down the damaged house, building the new house, reconnecting utility lines, and restoring the site around the new house. If you decide to move to a house outside the regulatory floodplain (option 3), your costs will be those for tearing down the damaged house, buying or building a house elsewhere, capping and abandoning the old utility lines, and restoring the old site.

The cost of tearing a house down, which is not a complex or difficult job, will be almost entirely for the disposal of the resulting debris. This cost can vary widely depending on the amount of debris, whether it can be buried at the demolition site or must be hauled to a licensed disposal site, and whether a dumping fee is required at the disposal site. The major costs associated with the demolition method will be for building or buying a house and will therefore depend on how and where you build or on the type of house you buy. Be sure to get a complete cost estimate before you begin a demolition project.

NOTE

As discussed in *Financial Assistance for Retrofitting* in Chapter 2, the cost of demolishing a substantially damaged house may be an eligible flood insurance claim under ICC coverage.

Summary

To protect your house from flooding, you may be able to use one or more of the retrofitting methods described in this chapter. However, as noted in this chapter, some retrofitting methods are probably inappropriate for your house, and some may not be allowed by your state or community. Also, if the substantial damage and substantial improvement requirements do not apply to your house, you may be faced with decisions about the level of protection you are willing to pay for and the level of risk you are willing to accept.

Chapter 4 will help you decide on a method. Then, depending on your decision, you can move on to Chapter 5, 6, or 7 for a detailed look at your preferred method.

Deciding Which Method Is Right for Your House

Introduction

With the information from Chapters 2 and 3, you are ready to decide which retrofitting method is right for your house. Your decision will be based primarily on legal requirements, the technical limitations of the methods, and cost. Other considerations might include such things as the appearance of the house after retrofitting and any inconvenience resulting from retrofitting. Making a decision involves four steps:

STEP 1

DETERMINE THE HAZARDS TO YOUR HOUSE
- Flood
- Wind
- Earthquake
- Others

STEP 2

INSPECT YOUR HOUSE
- Construction Type
- Foundation Type
- Lowest Floor Elevation
- Condition
- Other

STEP 3

CHECK WITH YOUR LOCAL OFFICIALS
- Hazards
- Regulations/ Codes
- Technical Guidance
- Financial Assistance

STEP 4

CONSULT A DESIGN PROFESSIONAL AND A CONTRACTOR
- Qualifications
- Site Inspection
- Cost Estimate
- Design
- Schedule

The four steps are described in the next section. At the end of this chapter you will find a retrofitting checklist that will help you work with local officials, design professionals, and retrofitting contractors. The checklist includes places where you can record the results of Steps 1 and 2, important questions you should ask, and decision making matrixes that will help you choose a retrofitting method. Before you go any further, you may want to make a copy of the checklist (see pages 76 through 82) so that you can begin filling it out.

NOTE

The results of Steps 1 and 2 will help your local official advise you and will also be useful when you consult a design professional or retrofitting contractor.

DEFINITION

A **tsunami** is a great sea wave produced by an earth movement or volcanic eruption.

Making Your Decision

Step 1 – Determine the Hazards to Your House

If you are using this guide, it is probably because your house has been damaged by flooding or because you know that your house is in a flood hazard area. Information about flooding in your area is available from local officials, as discussed later in Step 3. But if your house has been flooded, review what you already know. Look at the section of the checklist for Step 1. Answer as many of the questions as you can. Local officials, design professionals, and contractors can use the information you provide, along with the flood hazard information developed by the Federal Emergency Management Agency (FEMA) and other agencies and organizations, to advise you about your retrofitting options.

You also need to be aware of other hazards, such as high winds (see Figure 4-1), earthquakes (see Figure 4-2), fires, landslides, and **tsunamis.** If your house is in an area subject to one or more of these hazards, your retrofitting project should take the additional hazards into account. For example, as discussed in Chapter 3, elevating a house may make it more susceptible to high winds and earthquakes. As a result, the foundation may need to be reinforced and the connections between the foundation, walls, and roof may need to be strengthened as part of the retrofitting project. Depending on the nature of the hazards and your choice of retrofitting methods, State and local regulations may require that additional changes be made to your house, beyond those necessary for flood protection. Your local officials can tell you if such requirements apply and can give you more information.

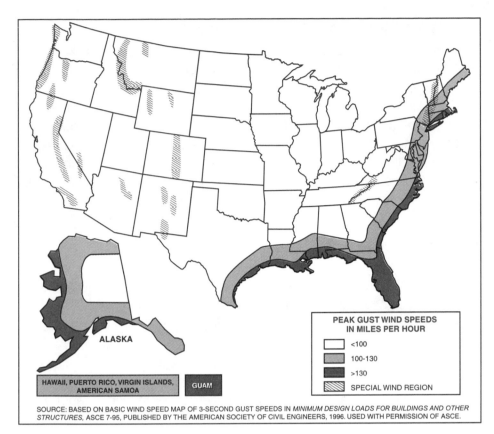

Figure 4-1
Peak gust wind speeds
in the United States.

PEAK GUST WIND SPEEDS
IN MILES PER HOUR

☐ <100
▨ 100-130
▧ >130
▨ SPECIAL WIND REGION

ALASKA

HAWAII, PUERTO RICO, VIRGIN ISLANDS,
AMERICAN SAMOA   GUAM

SOURCE: BASED ON BASIC WIND SPEED MAP OF 3-SECOND GUST SPEEDS IN *MINIMUM DESIGN LOADS FOR BUILDINGS AND OTHER STRUCTURES*, ASCE 7-95, PUBLISHED BY THE AMERICAN SOCIETY OF CIVIL ENGINEERS, 1996. USED WITH PERMISSION OF ASCE.

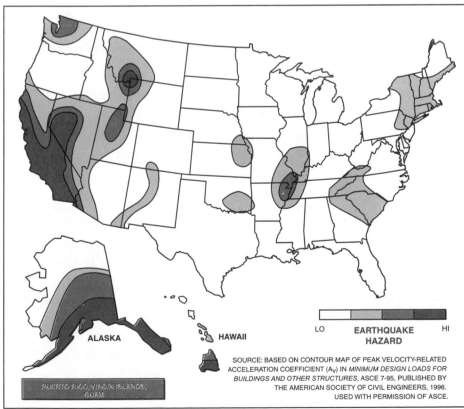

Figure 4-2
Earthquake hazards in
the United States.

ALASKA   HAWAII

PUERTO RICO, VIRGIN ISLANDS,
GUAM

LO   EARTHQUAKE   HI
            HAZARD

SOURCE: BASED ON CONTOUR MAP OF PEAK VELOCITY-RELATED
ACCELERATION COEFFICIENT (A_V) IN *MINIMUM DESIGN LOADS FOR BUILDINGS AND OTHER STRUCTURES*, ASCE 7-95, PUBLISHED BY THE AMERICAN SOCIETY OF CIVIL ENGINEERS, 1996. USED WITH PERMISSION OF ASCE.

WARNING

If you are retrofitting a house that has been substantially damaged or is being substantially improved, your community's floodplain management ordinance or law will <u>not</u> allow you to have a basement, as defined under the National Flood Insurance Program (NFIP). The NFIP regulations define a basement as "any area of the building having its floor subgrade on all sides." If your house has such a basement, you will be required to fill it in as part of any elevation project. Note that the NFIP definition of basement does not include what is typically referred to as a "walk-out-on-grade" basement, whose floor would be at or above adjacent grade on at least one side.

Step 2 – Inspect Your House

The discussion in Chapter 3 may have prompted you to begin thinking about your house, specifically how it is constructed and the type of foundation it has. Before you check with your local officials or consult a design professional and contractor, you should inspect your house and fill out the section of the checklist for Step 2. Four characteristics of your house that are particularly important in retrofitting are construction type, foundation type, lowest floor elevation, and condition. (When you fill out the portion of the checklist concerning construction and foundation type, you may want to refer to the descriptions that begin on page 35, in Chapter 3.)

Construction Type

As explained in Chapter 3, the construction type for most houses will be frame, masonry veneer, masonry, modular home, manufactured home, or a combination of two or more of these types. The following generalizations can be made about the effect of construction type on retrofitting:

- The most appropriate elevation technique for frame houses, and manufactured homes usually is to elevate on extended foundation walls or open foundations.

- The most commonly used elevation technique for masonry houses usually is either (1) to extend the walls of the house upward and raise the lower floor or (2) abandon the lowest floor and move the living area to an upper floor.

- Frame houses, masonry veneer houses, and manufactured homes are easier to relocate than masonry homes.

- Masonry and masonry veneer houses are usually easier to dry floodproof than other types of houses, because masonry is a more flood-resistant material than the materials used in other types of houses.

Foundation Type

As explained in Chapter 3, most houses of the construction types listed above are built on a basement, crawlspace, slab-on-grade, or open foundation or on a combination of two or more of these types. The following generalizations can be made about the effect of foundation type on retrofitting:

- Slab-on-grade houses are more difficult to elevate than houses on basement or crawlspace foundations.

- Elevating houses on basement foundations nomally involves elevating or relocating utility system components usually found in basements, such as furnaces and hot water heaters.

- Houses on basement foundations should not be dry flood-proofed or protected by levees or floodwalls unless an engineering evaluation conducted by a design professional shows that it is safe to do so. This precaution is necessary because neither dry floodproofing nor the construction of levees or floodwalls prevents saturated soils from pressing on basement walls. This pressure, which is unequalized because water is not allowed to enter the basement, can damage basement walls or even cause them to fail.

- For some houses on basement foundations, the same type of engineering evaluation is a necessary part of a wet floodproofing project. If the house is in an area where saturated soils begin to press on basement walls before water enters the basement, the unequalized pressure may damage walls or cause them to fail. If wet floodproofing is to be used in this situation, the engineering evaluation must show that the basement walls can resist the expected pressure.

Lowest Floor Elevation

As noted in Chapter 3, the "lowest floor" of your house, as defined by your community's floodplain management ordinance or law, is not necessarily the first or finished floor. For example, the lowest floor could be the floor of a basement or the floor of an attached garage. As shown in Figure 4-3, the location of your lowest floor can vary with foundation type. For houses that are to be elevated, wet floodproofed, or dry floodproofed, the difference between the elevation of the lowest floor and the Flood Protection Elevation (FPE) determines how high the house must be elevated or how high the wet or dry floodproofing protection must reach. In general, as the difference between the lowest floor elevation and the FPE increases, so does the cost of elevating, wet floodproofing, or dry floodproofing. This difference is particularly significant for dry floodproofing. As noted in Chapter 3, even masonry walls should not be dry floodproofed higher than 3 feet unless a structural evaluation by a design professional shows that it is safe to do so.

The elevation of your lowest floor can be established by a survey, which may be necessary as part of your retrofitting project. But even if you do not know your lowest floor elevation, you can estimate the difference between it and the FPE. If you haven't yet decided on an FPE, don't worry. Your conversations with your local officials, contractors, and design professionals will help you determine the level of flood protection you should provide. <u>Remember, if your house has been substantially damaged or is being substantially improved according to your community's floodplain management ordinance or law, your FPE must be at least equal to the Base Flood Elevation (BFE)</u>. As explained in Step 3, your local officials can tell you about this requirement.

Figure 4-3
Difference between flood level and lowest floor in houses on crawlspace and basement foundations.

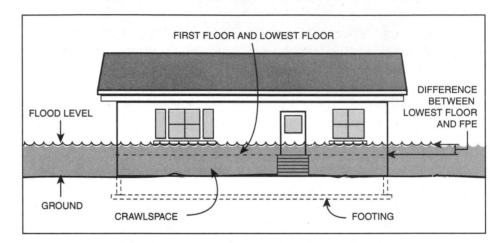

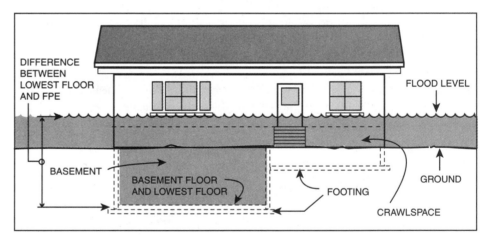

Condition

Your design professional or contractor should conduct a detailed inspection of your house before beginning any retrofitting work. You can help by first conducting your own assessment of the condition of your house and recording any information you have about past or current damage. This information may also be helpful to community officials who advise you about floodplain management and building code requirements and appropriate retrofitting methods.

If your house has been damaged by a flood, hurricane or other high-wind event, earthquake, fire, or other disaster, make a note of the extent of the damage, when it occurred, and whether it was repaired. If repairs were made, make a note of who made them and describe what was done. Any structural damage and repairs to walls, floors, foundations, and roofs is particularly important. You should also describe any damage resulting from other causes, such as foundation settlement, dry rot, and termite damage. Your goal is to give your design professional and contractor as much information as possible so that they can determine how the condition of your house will affect your choice of a retrofitting method.

Other Considerations

In addition to construction type, foundation type, and lowest floor elevation, you should make note of interior and exterior service equipment that must be protected as part of your retrofitting project. Interior service equipment must be protected if you wet floodproof your house. This equipment includes furnaces, heating and air conditioning ductwork, hot water heaters, large appliances, and electrical system components such as service panels, outlets, and switches. Exterior service equipment must be protected if you elevate, wet floodproof, or dry floodproof and, in some situations, if you build a levee or floodwall. This equipment includes air conditioning and heat pump compressors and electric and gas meters.

In a house that is dry floodproofed, all openings below the FPE must be sealed, including not only doors and windows but also the openings for water pipes, gas and electric lines, dryer vents, and sump pump discharge pipes. In a house that is dry floodproofed, wet floodproofed, or protected by a levee or floodwall, backflow valves must be installed on all water and sewer lines with openings below the FPE. These valves prevent flood waters and wastewater from backing up into your house. Chapter 8 describes how to protect interior and exterior service equipment.

Step 3 – Check with Your Local Officials

This is a particularly important step. Your local officials will have copies of the Flood insurance Study (FIS) and Flood Insurance Rate Map (FIRM) published for your community by FEMA. Your officials will be able to tell you whether your house is in your community's regulatory floodplain and, if so, the BFE at the location of your house. They may also have information about flood conditions near your house, including flow velocity, the potential for wave action and debris flow, rates of rise and fall, warning time, and duration of inundation.

Local officials will inform you of Federal, State, and local regulations, codes, and other requirements that can determine what retrofitting methods you will be allowed to use and how changes can be made to your house. They can also tell you about Federal, State, and local programs that provide financial assistance for homeowner retrofitting projects, and they can help

NOTE

Professional termite exterminators will often perform free or low-cost inspections for termite damage.

NOTE

Be sure to ask local officials about State or local freeboard requirements that may apply to your retrofitting project.

you determine whether you are eligible for such assistance. With the information you recorded in Steps 1 and 2, local officials may also be able to advise you about the most appropriate retrofitting method for your house. The officials you need to talk to will depend on how your community has assigned responsibilities for floodplain management and construction permitting. If you do not know who has these responsibilities in your community, you should begin with an official such as a city clerk, mayor, or county administrator.

Remember to contact your State Historic Preservation Office (see Appendix E) if your property is 50 or more years old and you are receiving Federal financial assistance for your retrofitting project. Your local officials may not be aware of this requirement if they do not normally deal with federally assisted projects.

When you talk to your local officials, be sure to do the following:

- Bring this guide with you.
- Bring your completed retrofitting checklist.
- Discuss what you already know about your house and the hazards that affect it.
- Work through the points listed in the section of the checklist for Step 3.
- Ask any other questions you may have.
- Work through the decision making matrix with the official. Use the matrix that applies to your situation: Substantial Damage/ Substantial Improvement or No Substantial Damage/No Substantial Improvement.
- Take notes about everything you discuss.

Remember that your goal is to find out what you can legally do to retrofit your house, identify the requirements you must comply with throughout the retrofitting process, and eliminate retrofitting methods that do not meet your needs. You may find that the restrictions and requirements of Federal, State, and local regulations will eliminate some retrofitting methods from consideration. Ultimately, your decision will be based on technical limitations of the methods, cost, and other considerations, such as the effect that retrofitting will have on the appearance of your house. The decision making matrix will help guide you through this process.

Your next step, whether you have chosen one method or are considering two or more, is to consult a properly licensed, bonded, and insured design professional and retrofitting contractor.

Step 4 – Consult a Design Professional and Contractor

To complete this step, you will need to know what types of services are required for your retrofitting project and how to evaluate and select contractors and design professionals.

You will probably need the services of a contractor regardless of the retrofitting method you select. The type of contractor you hire will depend on the method. You will probably also need to consult a design professional, such as a structural engineer. Alternatively, you can hire a general contractor who will arrange for all the necessary services, including those of a design professional. Table 4.1 shows the types of contractors and design professionals that may be required for each of the retrofitting methods.

Knowing the types of services required for your retrofitting project is important, but so is making sure that your design professional and contractor are reputable and competent.

If you have used a licensed design professional and a licensed contractor in the past and were satisfied with the work, use them again. Even if they do not provide the types of services you now need, they may be able to recommend someone who can. Otherwise, you can check the Yellow Pages or call or write to the professional association that represents the types of specialists you are looking for. Appendix F contains a list of the addresses and telephone numbers of several of these associations. They can usually give you a list of members in your area who specialize in the type of work you need. Before you hire a design professional or a contractor, you should check with your local Better Business Bureau, consumer protection agency, or licensing authorities. These organizations can tell you whether there have been any complaints about the quality of the design professional's or contractor's past work , including whether the work was completed on time.

Next, you will need to meet with the contractor and design professional to discuss your project. At the meeting, be sure you do the following:

- Provide the information you collected in Steps 1, 2, and 3.

- Ask the questions listed on the checklist at the end of this chapter, as well as any others you may have.

- Verify that the contractor is licensed, bonded, and insured as required by State and local laws.

- Verify that the design professional is licensed and registered in the state where the work will be done.

WARNING

Areas recovering from floods are often prime targets for less-than-honest business activities. Here are some pointers that can help you avoid problems:

<u>Beware</u> of "special deals" offered after a disaster by contractors you don't know.

<u>Beware</u> of unknown contractors who want to use your house as a "model home" for their work.

<u>Do not</u> sign any contract under pressure by a salesperson. Federal law requires a 3-day cooling-off period for unsolicited door-to-door sales of more than $25.

<u>Beware</u> if you are asked to pay cash on the spot instead of with a check made out to the name of a business.

REQUIREMENTS FOR CONTRACTOR AND DESIGN PROFESSIONAL SERVICES

Table 4.1

WARNING

Never sign a blank contract or one with blank spaces. You may want to have your attorney check the contract if a large amount of money is involved.

METHOD	NEED FOR CONTRACTOR AND/OR DESIGN PROFESSIONAL	PRIMARY SERVICES
ELEVATION	**Design Professional**	Evaluating the condition, stability, and strength of the existing foundation to determine whether it can support the increased load of the elevated house, including any wind and seismic loads
	Contractor: House Elevation Contractor	Disconnecting utilities, jacking the house up, increasing the height of the foundation, and connecting utilities
WET FLOOD-PROOFING	**Design Professional**	Designing any necessary replacements of vulnerable structural materials and relocated utility systems.
	Contractor: General Construction Contractor	Replacing vulnerable structural and finishing materials below the FPE with flood-resistant materials, raising utilities and appliances to a location above the FPE, and installing openings required to allow the entry of floodwaters
RELOCATION	**Design Professional**	Designing any new building, foundation, and site improvements that may be required, such as new utility systems.
	Contractor: House Moving Contractor	Jacking the house up, moving it to the new site, and installing it on the new foundation
	Contractor: General Construction Contractor	Preparing the new site (including grading, foundation construction, and utilities) and cleaning up the old site (including demolition)
DRY FLOOD-PROOFING	**Design Professional**	For masonry walls to be dry floodproofed higher than 3 feet and for masonry veneer or frame walls to be dry floodproofed higher than 2 feet, evaluating the condition, stability, and strength of the existing walls to determine whether they can withstand the pressure from flood waters at the FPE; designing or selecting flood shields for openings
	Contractor: General Construction Contractor	Applying waterproof sealants and membranes, installing flood shields over openings below the FPE, installing backflow valves in sewer and water lines, and, if necessary, bracing or modifying walls so that they can withstand the pressure from flood waters at the FPE
LEVEES AND FLOODWALLS	**Design Professional**	Assessing the adequacy of soils at the site, preparing the engineering design to ensure that the levee or floodwall, including any closures required, will be structurally stable under the expected flood loads and will be able to resist erosion, scour, and seepage
	Contractor: General Construction Contractor	Constructing the levee or flood wall
DEMOLITION	**Design Professional**	Designing any new building, foundation, and site improvements that may be required, such as new utility systems
	Contractor: Demolition Contractor	Disconnecting and capping utility lines, tearing down the damaged house, hauling away debris, and cleaning up the old site
	Contractor: General Construction Contractor	Building the new house on the new site (May also be able to do all demolition work.)

• Ask for proof of insurance. If the contractor or design professional does not have disability and worker's compensation insurance, you may be liable for accidents that occur on your property.

• Ask for references. Reputable contractors and design professionals should be willing to give you the names of previous customers. Call some of them and ask how well they were satisfied with the work. Ask if they would hire the contractor or design professional again.

• If you are trying to decide between two or more retrofitting methods, discuss your preferences and ask for more information.

Any contractor or design professional you hire will need to conduct a site visit to inspect your house and determine how the work should be carried out. During the site visit, you should expect your contractor or design professional to check the structural condition of your house and determine what changes will be required by the retrofitting method you choose. If you agree on a method and decide to proceed with the project, be sure to do the following:

• Get a written, signed, and dated estimate. It should cover everything you expect to be done. (Some contractors and design professionals will charge a fee for this service.)

• Decide whether you, the contractor, or the design professional will obtain the necessary permits.

• Ask for a warranty or guarantee. Any warranty or guarantee from the contractor or design professional should be written into the contract. The contract should clearly state the terms of the warranty or guarantee, who is responsible for honoring it (such as a manufacturer or the contractor), and how long it will remain valid.

• Get a written contract. It should be complete and clearly state all work to be done, the estimated cost, the payment schedule, and the expected start and completion dates for the work.

WARNING

Areas recovering from floods are often prime targets for less-than-honest business activities. Here are some pointers that can help you avoid problems:

<u>Check</u> with your local Better Business Bureau, consumer protection agency, or licensing authorities before you hire a contractor.

<u>Ask</u> contractors for references. A reputable contractor should be able to give you a list of past clients in your area who can comment on the quality of the contractor's work.

WARNING

Do not sign completion papers or make the final payment until all work is completed to your satisfaction.

RETROFITTING CHECKLIST

Use this checklist when you follow the four steps described in this chapter. The information you record here will help you work with local officials, contractors, and design professionals; use the decision making maxtrixes that follow this checklist; and decide which retrofitting method is right for your house.

Step 1 – Determine the Hazards to Your House

1. How long have you lived in your house? ___ years

2. Was your house ever flooded during that time? ___ yes ___ no
   (If your answer is yes, go to question 3; if your answer is no, go to question 14.)

3. How many times has your house been flooded? _____

4. What were the dates of flooding?

   Flood #1 _____
   Flood #2 _____
   Flood #3 _____
   Flood #4 _____
   Flood #5 _____

> For each flood, answer questions 5 through 13 as best you can.

5. To your knowledge, were frequencies assigned to any of the floods (for example, 50-year flood, 100-year flood)? If so, what were they?

   Flood #1 _____
   Flood #2 _____
   Flood #3 _____
   Flood #4 _____
   Flood #5 _____

6. How high did the flood water rise in your house? (If you can, state the height of the water above the lowest floor, including the basement floor.)

   Flood #1 _____
   Flood #2 _____
   Flood #3 _____
   Flood #4 _____
   Flood #5 _____

7. About how long did your house remain flooded? (You can give your answer in days, weeks, or months, as appropriate.)

   Flood #1 _____
   Flood #2 _____
   Flood #3 _____
   Flood #4 _____
   Flood #5 _____

8. Did you have any warning before your house was flooded? If so, how much warning?
    (You can give your answer in days or hours as appropriate.)

    Flood #1   ___ No Warning ___ Warning _____ Days / Hours
    Flood #2   ___ No Warning ___ Warning _____ Days / Hours
    Flood #3   ___ No Warning ___ Warning _____ Days / Hours
    Flood #4   ___ No Warning ___ Warning _____ Days / Hours
    Flood #5   ___ No Warning ___ Warning _____ Days / Hours

9. Did the flood waters cause scour and/or erosion around your house or elsewhere on your lot?
    If so, describe the effects.

    Flood #1   ___ No Erosion/Scour Occurred ___ Erosion/Scour Occurred
    Description _____
    _____

    Flood #2   ___ No Erosion/Scour Occurred ___ Erosion/Scour Occurred
    Description _____
    _____

    Flood #3   ___ No Erosion/Scour Occurred ___ Erosion/Scour Occurred
    Description _____
    _____

    Flood #4   ___ No Erosion/Scour Occurred ___ Erosion/Scour Occurred
    Description _____
    _____

    Flood #5   ___ No Erosion/Scour Occurred ___ Erosion/Scour Occurred
    Description _____
    _____

10. Was your house damaged by wave action or the impact of ice or other floodborne debris?
    If so, describe the damage.

    Flood #1   ___ No Waves or Debris ___ Waves ___ Debris
    Description of Damage _____
    _____

    Flood #2   ___ No Waves or Debris ___ Waves ___ Debris
    Description of Damage _____
    _____

    Flood #3   ___ No Waves or Debris ___ Waves ___ Debris
    Description of Damage _____
    _____

Flood #4   ___ No Waves or Debris ___ Waves ___ Debris

Description of Damage _____

_____

Flood #5   ___ No Waves or Debris ___ Waves ___ Debris

Description of Damage _____

_____

11. How difficult and/or expensive was cleaning up after the flood waters receded? (If you can, describe what you had to do to clean up both inside your house and around your lot, how long the cleanup took, and how much you spent on cleanup.)

Flood #1   Cleanup Description _____

_____ Cost $_____ Time _____

Flood #2   Cleanup Description _____

_____ Cost $_____ Time _____

Flood #3   Cleanup Description _____

_____ Cost $_____ Time _____

Flood #4   Cleanup Description _____

_____ Cost $_____ Time _____

Flood #5   Cleanup Description _____

_____ Cost $_____ Time _____

12. What was the total cost to repair all flood damage, not including the cleanup costs listed above?

Flood #1 $_____   **Flood #4** $_____
Flood #2 $_____   **Flood #5** $_____
Flood #3 $_____

13. What was the total value of all house contents (furnishings, belongings, etc.) damaged by flooding?

Flood #1 $_____   **Flood #4** $_____
Flood #2 $_____   **Flood #5** $_____
Flood #3 $_____

14. Is your house either in or near one of the shaded areas on the wind hazard map in Figure 4-1?
    ___ yes ____ no

15. Has your house ever been damaged by a hurricane or other high-wind event?
    ___ yes ___ no. If your answer is yes, note how many times and describe both the damage and the repairs made.

    _____
    _____
    _____
    _____
    _____
    _____
    _____
    _____
    _____
    _____

16. Is your house either in or near one of the shaded areas on the earthquake hazard map in Figure 4-2? ___ yes ___ no

17. Has your house ever been damaged by an earthquake? ___ yes ___ no. If your answer is yes, note how many times and describe both the damage and the repairs made.

    _____
    _____
    _____
    _____
    _____
    _____
    _____

18. Has your house ever been damaged by other hazard events, such as fires or landslides?
    ___ yes ___ no. If your answer is yes, note how many times and describe both the damage and the repairs made.

    _____
    _____
    _____
    _____
    _____
    _____
    _____

Step 2 – Inspect Your House

Provide as much of the following information as you can about your house.

1. When was your house built? ___

2. Construction type (see page 35.) Check as many as apply: ___ frame ___ masonry veneer ___ masonry ___ manufactured home

3. Foundation type (see page 36.) Check as many as apply: ___ basement (subgrade on all sides) ___ walkout-on-grade basement ___ crawlspace ___ slab-on-grade ___ piers ___ posts/columns ___ pilings

4. Describe any other damage and repairs to your house other than those you described in Step 1. Other damages would include foundation settlement, dry rot, and termite damage.

   _____
   _____
   _____
   _____
   _____
   _____

> To answer questions 5 through 9, you will need to have at least a rough idea of the FPE for your retrofitting project. If you don't have enough information to answer these questions now, go to Step 3 and determine your FPE when you talk with your local official(s).

5. Approximate difference between elevation of lowest floor (including basement) and Flood Protection Elevation (FPE) (see Figure 4-3): ___ feet

6. Interior utilities below the FPE (check as many as apply): ___ furnace ___ ductwork ___ hot water heater ___ electrical panel ___ electrical outlets ___ electrical switches ___ baseboard heaters ___ sump pumps
   other _____

7. Exterior utilities below the FPE (check as many as apply): ___ air conditioning /heat pump compressor ___ electric meter ___ fuel tank ___ septic tank ___ well ___ gas meter
   other _____

8. Major appliances below the FPE (check as many as apply): ___ washer ___ dryer ___ refrigerator ___ freezer
   other _____

9. How many drains (such as sink, tub, and floor drains) and toilets are below the FPE?

Step 3 – Check with Local Officials

When you meet with your local official(s), be sure to discuss the issues below. Also, make note of the information you receive. (You may find that you will need to talk with more than one person to get all the information you need.)

1. Explain your retrofitting needs, go over the information you recorded in Steps 1 and 2, and discuss any preferences you may have regarding the retrofitting methods described in Chapter 3.

2. Provide the official with photographs of your house and a copy of a plat map that shows the dimensions of your lot and the location of your house. If you do not have a plat map, ask how you can get one.

3. Ask whether your house is in the regulatory floodplain. If the answer is yes, ask what the BFE is at your house and whether your house is in the floodway or Coastal High hazard Area (V zone). Ask whether any restudies or revisions are underway that might provide updated flood hazard information for the area where your house is located. Also, ask for additional flood hazard information concerning characteristics such as flow velocity, the potential for wave action and debris flow, rates of rise and fall, warning time, and duration of inundation. This additional information may be useful to your design professional.

4. Ask whether your community's regulatory requirements concerning substantially damaged and substantially improved structures apply to your house. (See the definitions of substantial damage and substantial improvement on page 20 and the discussion on page 28.)

5. Ask whether your house is subject to high-winds, earthquakes, and other hazards, such as wildfires. Refer to the maps in Figures 4-1 and 4-2.

6. Ask whether your state and/or community enforces building codes or other regulations that could affect your retrofitting decision, including any floodplain management regulations more stringent than those required by the NFIP. For example, ask whether the state or community requires freeboard for flood protection measures.

7. In your discussion of building codes, ask whether retrofitting will require that you upgrade other components of your house (such as electrical and plumbing systems) to meet current code requirements.

8. Ask about the types of permits and fees that may be required in connection with any retrofitting methods you are considering.

9. Ask whether the official is aware of any Federal, State, or local historic preservation regulations affecting your property. Follow-up by contacting your State Historic Preservation Office (see Appendix E) to be sure that your retrofitting project is in compliance with all preservation laws.

10. Ask about Federal, State, and local programs that provide financial assistance for homeowner flood protection retrofitting projects. Ask whether you are eligible for assistance.

11. Go through the appropriate decision making matrix (see pages 83-86) with the official and discuss any questions you may have about the advantages and disadvantages of the alternative retrofitting methods.

12. Ask for any guidance that local officials can provide to help you find a good contractor or design professional.

Step 4 – Consult a Design Professional and Retrofitting Contractor

Initial Meeting

1. Explain your retrofitting needs; go over the information you recorded in Steps 1 and 2; discuss the results of your meeting with your local official(s), including the decision making matrix; and discuss any preferences you may have regarding retrofitting methods.

2. Verify that the contractor is licensed, bonded, and insured as required by State and local laws.

3. Verify that the design professional is licensed and registered in the state where the work will be done.

4. Ask for references and proof of proper bonds and insurance, including disability and workers' compensation.

5. Decide whether you, the design professional, or the contractor will be responsible for obtaining and managing the work of subcontractors and for obtaining all permits required by State and local agencies.

6. Schedule a site visit.

Site Visit

1. Ask the contractor or design professional to tell you about any characteristics of your house or lot that would affect your selection of a retrofitting method.

2. Once you decide on a retrofitting method, ask for a written estimate of the project cost and schedule.

Contract

1. If you are satisfied with the cost estimate and schedule, get a written, signed, and dated contract that describes the work to be done and states the estimated cost, the payment schedule, and the start and completion dates of the work.

2. Ask whether the contractor will provide a warranty or guarantee for the work performed. Any warranty or guarantee should be written into the contract. The contract should state the terms of the warranty or guarantee, who is responsible for honoring it, and how long it will remain valid.

Notes

_____

_____

_____

_____

_____

_____

_____

Decision Making Matrix

Condition: Substantial Damage / Substantial Improvement

This matrix can help you decide which retrofitting method best meets your needs. You may need guidance when using the matrix, so take it with you when you meet with local officials and contractors/design professionals.

Because your house either has been substantially damaged or is being substantially improved, the National Flood Insurance Program regulations limit your choice of retrofitting methods to elevation, relocation, wet floodproofing, or demolition. Regulations, ordinances, or laws established by other agencies and organizations may further limit your choice. Also, you may have already decided that one or more methods will not meet your needs. The first step in using the matrix is to identify any methods eliminated by regulations or by your own needs. Mark each eliminated method by placing an "X" in the box directly below the name of the method (on the line labeled "Prohibited by Federal, State, or Local Regulations or Eliminated by Law"). An "X" in this row means that the method will not be considered in your decision.

The next step is to evaluate the remaining methods (those without an "X" under their names). Your evaluation will be based on the factors listed on the left hand side of the matrix. (The factors are explained on the back of this page.) For each evaluation factor under each method, discuss your concerns with your local official, design professional, and contractor. If your concerns cannot be resolved, place an "X" in the appropriate box. For example, if you decide that you would not be satisfied with the appearance of your house if it were elevated on extended foundation walls, you would place an "X" in the box on the *Appearance* line under the heading *Elevation on Extended Foundation Walls*. After you have worked through the entire matrix, add the number of "X's" under each method and show the sum on the *Total "X's"* line. The method with the lowest total is the one that best meets your requirements.

RETROFITTING METHODS
Substantially Damaged or Substantially Improved Houses

EVALUATION FACTORS	ELEVATION			RELOCATION	WET FLOOD-PROOFING[1]	DEMOLITION
	Elevation On Extended Foundation Walls	Elevation On Open Foundation	New Living Area Over Abandoned First Floor			
Prohibited by Federal, State, or Local Regulations or Eliminated by Homeowner						
Appearance						
Cost						
Accessibility						
Code-Required Upgrades						
Human Intervention						
Other						
TOTAL "X's"						

[1] Wet floodproofing is allowed only if the part of your house below the BFE is used solely for parking, storage, or building access.

EVALUATION FACTORS

Federal, State, and Local Restrictions — Federal, State, and local regulations may restrict a homeowner's choice of retrofitting measures. Such regulations may include State and local building codes, floodplain management ordinances or laws, zoning ordinances, Federal regulations concerning the alteration of buildings classified as historic structures, deed restrictions, and the covenants of homeowners associations. The homeowner and the homeowner's contractor or design professional should check with community officials to determine whether such regulations apply.

Appearance — The final appearance of a house and property after retrofitting will depend largely on the retrofitting method used and the Flood Protection Elevation (FPE). For example, elevating a house several feet will change its appearance much more than elevating only 1 or 2 feet, and a house elevated on an open foundation will not look the same as a house elevated on extended foundation walls. However, a change in appearance will not necessarily be a change for the worse. The homeowner should discuss the potential effects of each method with local officials and with the contractor or design professional.

Cost — The cost of retrofitting will depend largely on the retrofitting method used and the FPE. For some methods, the construction type (frame, masonry, etc.) and foundation type (crawlspace, slab, etc.) will also affect the cost. In general, costs will increase as the FPE increases, but there may be tradeoffs between alternative methods. For example, elevating may be less expensive than relocation when a house is raised only 1 or 2 feet, but may become more expensive at greater heights.

Accessibility — Accessibility refers to how easy or difficult it is to routinely reach and enter the house after the retrofitting project is completed. The retrofitting methods described in this guide affect accessibility in different ways. For example, elevating a house will usually require the addition of stairs, which may be unacceptable to some homeowners. Wet floodproofing will have little if any affect on accessibility. The effect of relocation on accessibility will depend on the location and configuration of the new site.

Code-Required Upgrades   State and local regulations may require that a retrofitted house be upgraded to meet current code requirements that were not in effect when the house was built. Portions of the electrical, plumbing, and heating/ventilation/air conditioning systems could be affected. For example, the electrical panel might have to be upgraded from fuses to circuit breakers. These changes are required for the safety of the homeowner. Other code-required upgrades include those necessary for increased energy efficiency. Any required upgrade can add to the scope and cost of the retrofitting project. The homeowner and the homeowner's contractor or design professional should check with community officials to determine whether such regulations apply.

Human Intervention — For retrofitting methods that require human intervention, homeowners must be willing, able, and prepared to take the necessary action, such as operating a closure mechanism in a floodwall or placing flood barriers across the doors of a dry floodproofed house. Also, the homeowner must always have adequate warning of a coming flood and must be at home or near enough to reach the house and take the necessary action before flood waters arrive. If these conditions cannot be met, retrofitting methods that require human intervention should be eliminated from consideration.

Other — Homeowners may need to consider other factors, such as the availability of Federal, State, and local financial assistance; the current value of the house vs. the inconvenience and cost of retrofitting; the amount of time required to complete the retrofitting project; and the need to move out of the house during construction (including the availability and cost of alternative housing).

Decision Making Matrix

Condition: <u>NO</u> Substantial Damage / <u>NO</u> Substantial Improvement

This matrix can help you decide which retrofitting method best meets your needs. You may need guidance when using the matrix, so take it with you when you meet with local officials and contractors/design professionals.

Because your house has **NOT** been substantially damaged and is **NOT** being substantially improved, the National Flood Insurance Program regulations do not prohibit your use of any of the methods described in this guide. However, regulations, ordinances, or laws established by other agencies and organizations may. Also, you may have already decided that one or more methods will not meet your needs. The first step in using the matrix is to identify any methods eliminated by regulations or by your own needs. Mark each eliminated method by placing an "X" in the box directly below the name of the method (on the line labeled "Prohibited by Federal, State, or Local Regulations or Eliminated by Law"). An "X" in this row means that the method will not be considered in your decision.

The next step is to evaluate the remaining methods (those without an "X" under their names). Your evaluation will be based on the factors listed on the left hand side of the matrix. (The factors are explained on the back of this page.) For each evaluation factor under each method, discuss your concerns with your local official, design professional, and contractor. If your concerns cannot be resolved, place an "X" in the appropriate box. For example, if you decide that you would not be satisfied with the appearance of your house if it were elevated on extended foundation walls, you would place an "X" in the box on the *Appearance* line under the heading *Elevation on Extended Foundation Walls*. After you have worked through the entire matrix, add the number of "X's" under each method and show the sum on the *Total "X's"* line. The method with the lowest total is probably the one that best meets your requirements.

EVALUATION FACTORS	ELEVATION							
	Elevation On Extended Foundation Walls	Elevation On Open Foundation	New Living Area Over Abandoned First Floor	RELOCATION	DRY FLOOD-PROOFING	WET FLOOD-PROOFING	LEVEES OR FLOOD-WALLS	DEMOLITION
RETROFITTING METHODS for Houses that are NOT Substantially Damaged or Improved								
Prohibited by Federal, State, or Local Regulations or Eliminated by Homeowner								
Appearance								
Cost								
Accessibility								
Code-Required Upgrades								
Human Intervention								
Other								
TOTAL "X's"								

EVALUATION FACTORS

Federal, State, and Local Restrictions — Federal, State, and local regulations may restrict the homeowner's choice of retrofitting measures. Such regulations may include State and local building codes, floodplain management ordinance or laws, zoning ordinances, Federal regulations concerning the alteration of buildings classified as historic structures, deed restrictions, and the covenants of homeowners associations. The homeowner and the homeowner's contractor or design professional should check with community officials to determine whether such regulations apply.

Appearance — The final appearance of a house and property after retrofitting will depend largely on the retrofitting method used and the Flood Protection Elevation (FPE). For example, elevating a house several feet will change its appearance much more than elevating only 1 or 2 feet, and wet floodproofing will change its appearance very little. However, a change in appearance will not necessarily be a change for the worse. The homeowner should discuss the potential effects of each method with local officials and with the contractor or design professional.

Cost — The cost of retrofitting will depend largely on the retrofitting method used and the FPE. For some methods, the construction type (frame, masonry, etc.) and foundation type (crawlspace, slab, etc.) will also affect the cost. In general, costs will increase as the FPE increases, but there may be tradeoffs between alternative methods. For example, elevating may be less expensive than relocation when a house is raised only 1 or 2 feet, but may become more expensive at greater heights. Other costs include those for both routine and long-term maintenance.

Accessibility — Accessibility refers to how easy or difficult it is to routinely reach and enter the house after the retrofitting project is completed. The retrofitting methods described in this guide affect accessibility in different ways. For example, elevating a house will usually require the addition of stairs, which may be unacceptable to some homeowners. Levees and floodwalls can make access more difficult unless they are equipped with openings, which require human intervention (see below). Wet floodproofing and dry floodproofing will have little if any affect on accessibility. The effect of relocation on accessibility will depend on the location and configuration of the new site.

Code-Required Upgrades — State and local regulations may require that a retrofitted house be upgraded to meet current code requirements that were not in effect when the house was built. Portions of the electrical, plumbing, and heating/ventilation/air conditioning systems could be affected. For example, the electrical panel might have to be upgraded from fuses to circuit breakers. These changes are required for the safety of the homeowner. Other code-required upgrades include those necessary for increased energy efficiency. Any required upgrade can add to the scope and cost of the retrofitting project. The homeowner and the homeowner's contractor or design professional should check with community officials to determine whether such regulations apply.

Human Intervention — For retrofitting methods that require human intervention, homeowners must be willing, able, and prepared to take the necessary action, such as operating a closure mechanism in a floodwall or placing flood barriers across the doors of a dry floodproofed house. Also, the homeowner must always have adequate warning of a coming flood and must be at home or near enough to reach the house and take the necessary action before flood waters arrive. If these conditions cannot be met, retrofitting methods that require human intervention should be eliminated from consideration.

Other — Homeowners may need to consider other factors, such as the availability of Federal, State, and local financial assistance; the current value of the house vs. the inconvenience and cost of retrofitting; the amount of time required to complete the retrofitting project; and the need to move out of the house during construction (including the availability and cost of alternative housing).

Elevating Your House

Introduction

One of the most common retrofitting methods is elevating a house to a required or desired Flood Protection Elevation (FPE). When a house is properly elevated, the living area will be above all but the most severe floods (such as the 500-year flood). Several elevation techniques are available. In general, they involve (1) lifting the house and building a new, or extending the existing, foundation below it or (2) leaving the house in place and either building an elevated floor within the house or adding a new upper story.

During the elevation process, most frame, masonry veneer, and masonry houses are separated from their foundations, raised on hydraulic jacks, and held by temporary supports while a new or extended foundation is constructed below. The living area is raised and only the foundation remains exposed to flooding. This technique works well for houses originally built on basement, crawlspace, and open foundations. When houses are lifted with this technique, the new or extended foundation can consist of either continuous walls or separate piers, posts, columns, or pilings. Masonry houses are more difficult to lift, primarily because of their design, construction, and weight, but lifting these homes is possible. In fact, numerous contractors throughout the United States regularly perform this work.

A variation of this technique is used for frame, masonry veneer, and masonry houses on slab-on-grade foundations. In these houses, the slab forms both the floor of the house and either all or a major part of the foundation. Elevating these houses is easier if the house is left attached to the slab and both are lifted together. After the house and slab are lifted, a new foundation is constructed below the slab.

For masonry houses on slab-on-grade foundations, some homeowners find it easier to use one of two alternative elevation techniques, in which the house is left on its original foundation. One technique is to remove the roof, extend the walls of the house upward, replace the roof, and then build a new elevated living area inside. The second is to abandon the existing lower enclosed area (the level with the slab floor) and move the living space to an existing or newly constructed upper floor. The abandoned lower enclosed area is then used only for parking, storage, and access to the house.

In both of these techniques, portions of the original walls will be below the FPE. This approach is appropriate for masonry construction, which is naturally flood-resistant, but not for frame construction, which could easily be damaged by flood waters.

This chapter describes and illustrates the various elevation methods and discusses the most important considerations regarding elevation.

Considerations

Amount of Elevation

The amount of elevation required is determined by the FPE you have chosen. For example, if your FPE is equal to the Base Flood Elevation (BFE), you will need to elevate your house so that the lowest floor is at or above that elevation (see Figure 5-1). As explained earlier, if your house has been substantially damaged or is being substantially improved, your community's floodplain management ordinance or law will require that your lowest floor be elevated to or above the BFE.

If substantial damage and substantial improvement do not apply, you may be able to elevate to any height you wish. But, keep in mind that raising your house to an elevation below BFE not only provides less protection but also results in little, if any, decrease in the flood insurance rate. Regardless of whether your house has been substantially damaged or is being substantially improved, you should consider incorporating at least 1 foot of freeboard into your FPE (as shown in Figure 5-1).

Figure 5-1
As shown in the cutaway view, the lowest floor is above the flood level. When at least 1 foot of freeboard is provided, only the foundation is exposed to flooding.

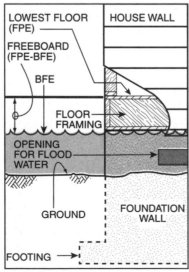

Elevating a house up to 3 or 4 feet above the existing ground level usually will not have a great effect on its appearance and will require only minimal landscaping and regrading. If you plan to elevate more than 4 feet above the existing grade, you should consider elevating your house a full story, so that you can use the space below the elevated house for parking, storage, or building access (see Figure 5-2).

Figure 5-2
This house in Atlanta, Georgia, was elevated one full story. The garage and storage area are at the house's original elevation.

WARNING

If you are elevating a house that has been substantially damaged or is being substantially improved, your community's floodplain management ordinance or law will <u>not</u> allow you to have a basement, as defined under the NFIP. The NFIP regulations define a basement as "any area of the building having its floor subgrade on all sides." If your house has such a basement, you will be required to fill it in as part of any elevation project. Note that the National Flood Insurance Program (NFIP) definition of basement does not include what is typically referred to as a "walkout-on-grade" basement, whose floor would be at or above grade on at least one side.

WARNING

If your house has been substantially damaged or is being substantially improved and is in a Coastal High Hazard Area (Zone V, VE, or V1-V30 on the Flood Insurance Rate Map (FIRM) for your community), your community's floodplain management ordinance or law will require that the bottom of the lowest horizontal structural member (rather than the lowest floor) be elevated to or above the BFE. In many houses, the lowest horizontal structural member is a beam that supports the framing of the lowest floor. With the exception of *Elevating on an Open Foundation*, described at the end of this chapter, the elevation techniques presented in this guide are <u>not</u> appropriate for houses in Coastal High Hazard Areas. If you have any doubt about the type of flood hazards that may affect your house, check with your local officials.

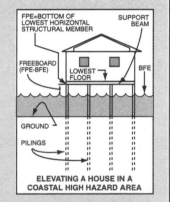

FPE=BOTTOM OF LOWEST HORIZONTAL STRUCTURAL MEMBER　　SUPPORT BEAM

FREEBOARD (FPE-BFE)　　LOWEST FLOOR　　BFE

GROUND

PILINGS

ELEVATING A HOUSE IN A COASTAL HIGH HAZARD AREA

Existing Foundation

In general, the most economical approach to elevating a house is to use as much of the existing foundation as possible. Although some elevation methods do not allow this approach, most do. If you choose one of the latter, a design professional must evaluate the ability of your existing foundation to support the loads that will be imposed by the elevated house and, as discussed in the next section, the loads expected to result from flooding and other hazards at the site. If changes must be made to the foundation to increase its strength and stability, they can be made as part of your retrofitting project, but they can increase both the cost of the project and the time required to complete it.

The type of foundation on which your house was originally built (basement, crawlspace, slab-on-grade, piers, posts, pilings) also can affect the elevation process. This issue is discussed later in this chapter, in the section *The Elevation Techniques*.

Hazards

Because so many elevation techniques are available, elevation is practical for almost any flood situation, but the flooding conditions and other hazards at the house site must be examined so that the most suitable technique can be determined. Regardless of the elevation technique used, the foundation of the elevated house must be able to withstand, at a minimum, the expected loads from hydrostatic pressure, hydrodynamic pressure, and debris impact. It must also be able to resist undermining by any expected erosion and scour.

If you are elevating a house in an area subject to high winds, earthquakes, or other hazards, a design professional should determine whether the elevated house, including its foundation, will be able to withstand all of the horizontal and vertical forces expected to act on it. In making this determination, the design professional must consider a number of factors, including the structure and condition of the house, the soil conditions at the site, the proposed elevation technique, and the hazards at the site. The conclusion may be that additional modifications must be made during the retrofitting project.

WARNING

Placing fill in floodways and Coastal High Hazard Areas is normally prohibited. Check with your local officials about State and local requirements concerning the use of fill.

Access

Elevating a house usually requires that new means of access be provided. For example, if your entry doors were originally at ground level, new staircases, elevators, or ramps will have to be built. When an attached garage is elevated, providing access for vehicles may require changes to portions of your lot, such as building a new, elevated driveway on earth fill that ties into high ground elsewhere. This solution can be practical when the amount of elevation required is no more than 2 or 3 feet. As noted earlier, when the amount of elevation reaches 4 or more feet, you should consider elevating your house a full story so that you can use the lower level for parking and avoid the need for an elevated driveway.

The need to provide new means of access is often the main objection that homeowners have to elevating. But functional and attractive solutions to this problem can usually be developed, as shown in Figure 2-2 in Chapter 2 and Figure 5-3.

Figure 5-3
With attention to detail and planning, homeowners have created attractive retrofitted houses.

House Size, Design, and Shape

In general, the larger the house and the more complex its design and shape, the more difficult it will be to lift on jacks. Multistory houses are more difficult to stabilize during the lifting process, and as the dimensions and weight of a house increase, so do the required numbers of jacks and other pieces of lifting equipment. Exterior wall coverings such as stucco and brick veneer complicate the lifting process because they must either be removed or braced so that they will stay in place when the house is lifted. Houses with simple square or rectangular shapes are easier to lift than those with attached garages, porches, wings, or additions, which often must be detached and lifted separately, especially if they are built on separate foundations.

Before a house is lifted, a design professional should inspect it to verify its structural soundness. All the structural members and their connections must be able to withstand the stresses imposed by the lifting process. Lifting an unsound house can lead to potentially expensive damage.

Service Equipment

Before your house is elevated, all utility lines (water, sewer, gas, electric, telephone, etc.) must be disconnected. At the end of the project, the lines will be reconnected and any landscaping that may be necessary will be completed. If you elevate your house on an open foundation, utility lines that enter the house from below may be exposed to damage from flooding and below-freezing temperatures. Protecting utility lines in these situations usually involves anchoring them securely to vertical foundation members and, if necessary, insulating them. All service equipment outside the

DEFINITION

Service equipment includes utility systems, heating and cooling systems, and large appliances.

house, such as air conditioning and heat pump compressors and gas and electric meters, must be elevated to or above the FPE. In houses with basements, any service equipment originally installed in the basement will have to be raised above the FPE, which may require relocation to an upper floor. Chapter 8 discusses the protection of service equipment.

The Elevation Techniques

The elevation techniques and their application to different types of houses are discussed in the following sections.

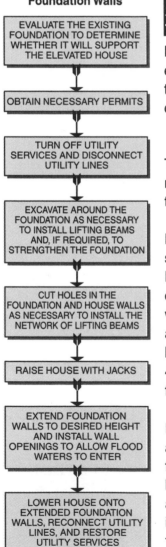

PROCESS:
Elevating on Extended
Foundation Walls

EVALUATE THE EXISTING FOUNDATION TO DETERMINE WHETHER IT WILL SUPPORT THE ELEVATED HOUSE

OBTAIN NECESSARY PERMITS

TURN OFF UTILITY SERVICES AND DISCONNECT UTILITY LINES

EXCAVATE AROUND THE FOUNDATION AS NECESSARY TO INSTALL LIFTING BEAMS AND, IF REQUIRED, TO STRENGTHEN THE FOUNDATION

CUT HOLES IN THE FOUNDATION AND HOUSE WALLS AS NECESSARY TO INSTALL THE NETWORK OF LIFTING BEAMS

RAISE HOUSE WITH JACKS

EXTEND FOUNDATION WALLS TO DESIRED HEIGHT AND INSTALL WALL OPENINGS TO ALLOW FLOOD WATERS TO ENTER

LOWER HOUSE ONTO EXTENDED FOUNDATION WALLS, RECONNECT UTILITY LINES, AND RESTORE UTILITY SERVICES

Elevating on Extended Foundation Walls

Frame, masonry veneer, and masonry houses can all be elevated on extended foundation walls. As discussed in the following sections, the technique used for houses on basement and crawlspace foundations differs from that used for houses on slab-on-grade foundations.

Houses on Basement Foundations and Crawlspace Foundations

The elevation process is the same for frame, masonry veneer, and masonry houses on basement and crawlspace foundations. Figures 5-4a through 5-4d illustrate the process.

First, holes are made at intervals in the foundation wall so that a series of steel I-beams can be installed at critical points under the floor framing (see Figure 5-4a). If the foundation walls are made of concrete blocks, the lifting contractor can remove individual blocks to create the required holes. If the walls are made of poured concrete, the holes will be cut out. The I-beams are placed so that they run perpendicular to the floor joists. A second set of beams is then placed below and perpendicular to the first set (see Figure 5-4a). The two sets of beams extend the width and length of the house and form a cradle that supports the house as it is being raised.

In Figure 5-4a, the foundation walls are shown as extending far enough above the ground surface to provide easy access to the area below the floor framing. In some houses, however, the foundation walls will not be this high. To lift such a house, the contractor must first dig trenches at intervals around the foundation. The I-beams are then lowered into the trenches and inserted below the floor framing. The contractor may also have to dig holes for the lifting jacks, as shown in the figure. The number of jacks needed will depend on the size, shape, and type of house being lifted.

Once the beams and jacks are in place, the elevation process begins. The jacks will extend only so high; so at intervals during the process, the house and jacks are supported temporarily on cribbing while the jacks are raised (see Figure 5-4b). After the house is elevated high enough, it is again supported on cribbing while the foundation walls are extended to the desired height with concrete blocks or poured concrete (see Figure 5-4c). The house is then lowered onto the extended foundation walls, the I-beams are removed, and the holes where the beams passed through are filled. An important part of the project is installing openings in the foundation walls, no higher than 1 foot above the ground, so that flood waters can enter and equalize the internal and external hydrostatic pressures. As shown in Figure 5-4c, the contractor can create these openings by only partially filling the I-beam holes.

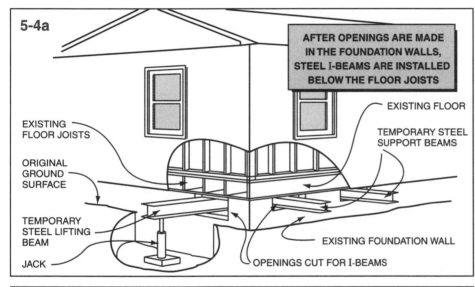

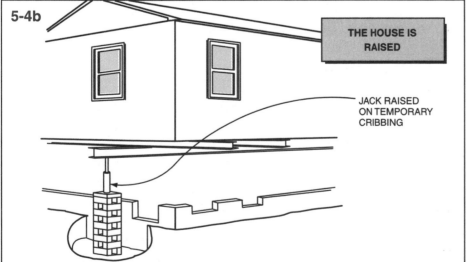

Figures 5-4a through 5-4d. Elevating a basement or crawlspace foundation house on extended foundation walls.

NOTE

For more information about openings requirements, refer to FEMA Technical Bulletin 1-93, *Openings in Foundation Walls for Buildings Located in Special Flood Hazard Areas, and FEMA 259, Engineering Principles and Practices for Retrofitting Flood Prone Residential Buildings.*

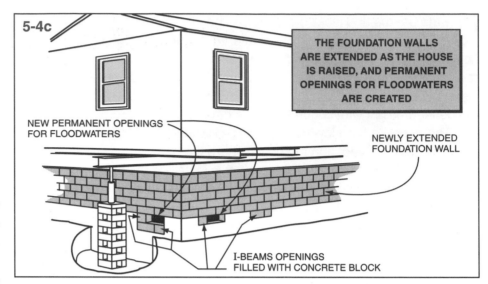

5-4c

THE FOUNDATION WALLS ARE EXTENDED AS THE HOUSE IS RAISED, AND PERMANENT OPENINGS FOR FLOODWATERS ARE CREATED

NEW PERMANENT OPENINGS FOR FLOODWATERS

NEWLY EXTENDED FOUNDATION WALL

I-BEAMS OPENINGS FILLED WITH CONCRETE BLOCK

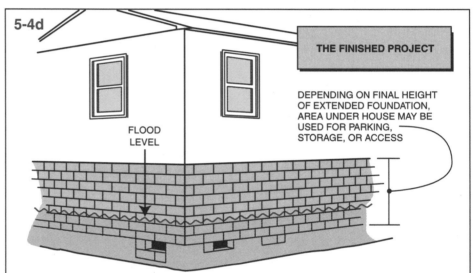

5-4d

THE FINISHED PROJECT

FLOOD LEVEL

DEPENDING ON FINAL HEIGHT OF EXTENDED FOUNDATION, AREA UNDER HOUSE MAY BE USED FOR PARKING, STORAGE, OR ACCESS

Houses on Slab-On-Grade Foundations

Frame, masonry veneer, and masonry houses on slab-on-grade foundations are also lifted with hydraulic jacks and a network of steel I-beams. However, design and construction differences between slab-on-grade houses and those on other types of foundations present special difficulties and require a different lifting technique.

The floor of a house on a slab-on-grade foundation, is formed by the slab rather than the wood joist and beam framing found in houses on crawlspace and basement foundations. The slab is usually 4 to 6 inches thick and is often reinforced with wire mesh. As shown in the cross section view in Figure 5-5, the slab can be supported by foundation walls and footings or by a thickened edge created when the slab is poured.

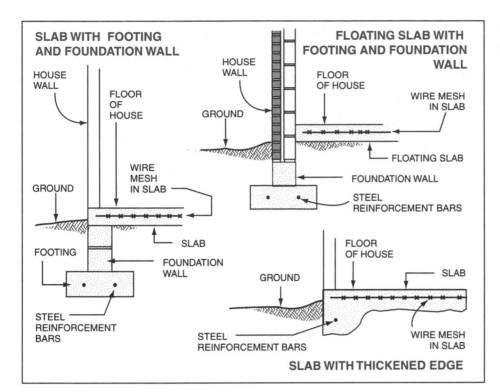

Figure 5-5
Slab foundation types.

Because the slab forms the floor of the house, and occasionally the foundation as well, elevating the house is easier if the house and slab are lifted together. But this technique is more difficult than that used for houses on basement and crawlspace foundations and should be performed only by a highly skilled contractor with extensive experience in lifting slab-on-grade houses. The wire mesh in the slab is intended to prevent shrinkage cracking during the original construction of the slab; it is not intended to provide structural strength. As a result, the contractor must take extreme care during the lifting process to avoid breaking the slab and compromising the structural integrity of the house.

The elevation process (see Figures 5-6a through 5-6d) is similar to that used for houses on basement and crawlspace foundations, except that the I-beams must be placed below the slab, which is at ground level. So, the contractor must dig trenches at intervals around the foundation, and tunnel under the slab. The I-beams are lowered into the trenches and moved into place beneath the slab through the tunnels (see Figure 5-6a).

The contractor must also dig holes for the lifting jacks because they have to be placed below the beams. Once the beams and jacks are in place, the lifting process begins. As shown in Figures 5-6b and 5-6c, the house is lifted and a new foundation is constructed below it.

Figures 5-6a through 5-6d. Elevating a slab-on-grade house with the slab attached

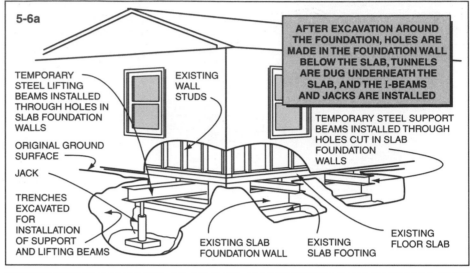

5-6a

AFTER EXCAVATION AROUND THE FOUNDATION, HOLES ARE MADE IN THE FOUNDATION WALL BELOW THE SLAB, TUNNELS ARE DUG UNDERNEATH THE SLAB, AND THE I-BEAMS AND JACKS ARE INSTALLED

TEMPORARY STEEL LIFTING BEAMS INSTALLED THROUGH HOLES IN SLAB FOUNDATION WALLS

EXISTING WALL STUDS

TEMPORARY STEEL SUPPORT BEAMS INSTALLED THROUGH HOLES CUT IN SLAB FOUNDATION WALLS

ORIGINAL GROUND SURFACE

JACK

TRENCHES EXCAVATED FOR INSTALLATION OF SUPPORT AND LIFTING BEAMS

EXISTING SLAB FOUNDATION WALL

EXISTING SLAB FOOTING

EXISTING FLOOR SLAB

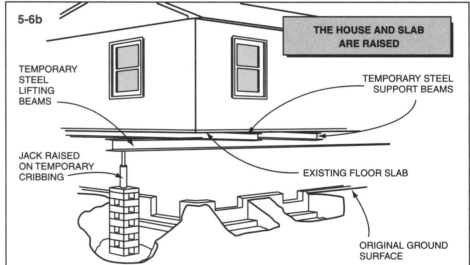

5-6b

THE HOUSE AND SLAB ARE RAISED

TEMPORARY STEEL LIFTING BEAMS

TEMPORARY STEEL SUPPORT BEAMS

JACK RAISED ON TEMPORARY CRIBBING

EXISTING FLOOR SLAB

ORIGINAL GROUND SURFACE

NOTE

For more information about openings requirements, refer to FEMA Technical Bulletin 1-93, *Openings in Foundation Walls for Buildings Located in Special Flood Hazard Areas,* and *FEMA 259, Engineering Principles and Practices for Retrofitting Flood Prone Residential Buildings.*

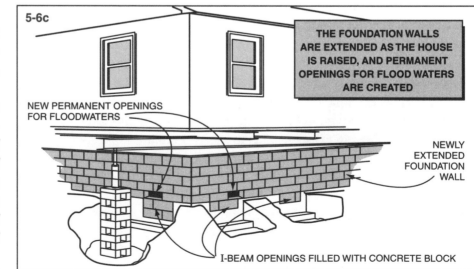

5-6c

THE FOUNDATION WALLS ARE EXTENDED AS THE HOUSE IS RAISED, AND PERMANENT OPENINGS FOR FLOOD WATERS ARE CREATED

NEW PERMANENT OPENINGS FOR FLOODWATERS

NEWLY EXTENDED FOUNDATION WALL

I-BEAM OPENINGS FILLED WITH CONCRETE BLOCK

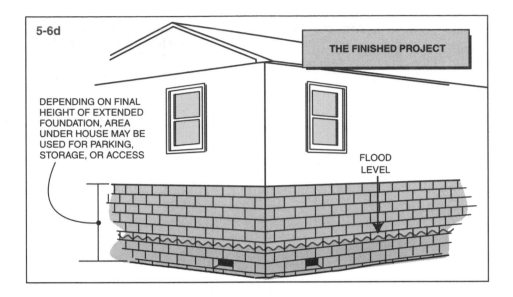

5-6d

DEPENDING ON FINAL HEIGHT OF EXTENDED FOUNDATION, AREA UNDER HOUSE MAY BE USED FOR PARKING, STORAGE, OR ACCESS

THE FINISHED PROJECT

FLOOD LEVEL

If the slab was originally supported by foundation walls and footings (see upper and left-hand illustrations in Figure 5-5), the contractor may be able to leave them in place and extend the existing walls upward. This approach will be possible only when a design professional determines that the original foundation walls and footings are strong enough to support the elevated house and slab under the expected flood, wind, earthquake, and other loads. If the slab was originally supported by its own thickened edge (shown in the lower illustration in Figure 5-5), a completely new foundation must be constructed.

In both situations, the contractor must construct not only foundation walls under the perimeter of the slab but also additional vertical foundation members, such as piers, at several locations under the slab. These additional foundation members are necessary because slabs are designed to rest directly on the ground, not to support the weight of the house.

A less frequently used technique for elevating slab-on-grade houses is to separate the house from the slab, lift the house, and leave the slab on the ground. Because the slab is not lifted, the I-beams are inserted through openings cut into the walls of the house above the slab rather than below it. To enable the beams to lift the house, the contractor attaches horizontal wood bracing to the interior and exterior walls at the tops of the openings (see Figure 5-7).

Figure 5-7
Elevating a slab-on-grade house without the slab.

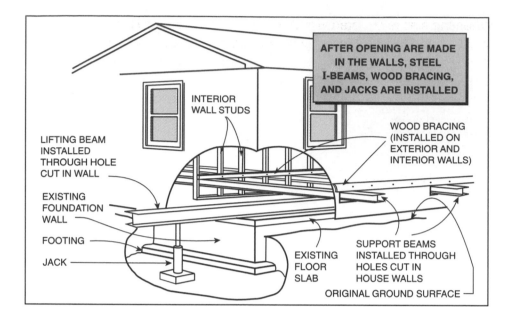

When the beams are jacked up, they push against the bracing, which distributes the lifting force equally across the walls. The bracing also supports the walls, which lack the structural stability that would otherwise be provided when the walls and floor are left attached. Without bracing, the walls could twist, bend, or collapse when the house is lifted. If a design professional determines that the original slab is strong enough to support the elevated house under the expected flood, wind, earthquake, and other loads, the slab may be left in place and the new foundation walls built on top. Otherwise, the slab must be cut back and a completely new foundation constructed, as shown in Figure 5-8.

Figure 5-8
Building a new foundation for a slab-on-grade house

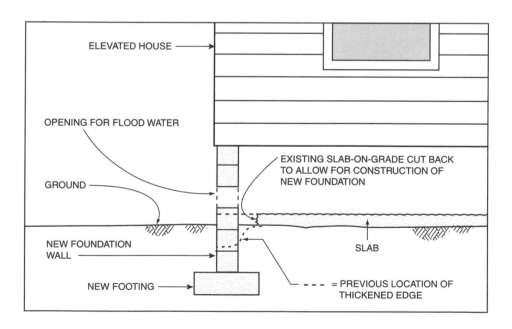

When the slab is not lifted with the house, a new, elevated floor must be constructed. The new floor can be a wood-framed floor like that typically found in a house on a basement or crawlspace foundation, or it can be a new, elevated concrete slab. Building a new slab floor involves placing fill dirt on top of the old slab and pouring a new slab on top of the fill. Although the old slab is left in place, it is usually broken up so that it will not be forced up by the buoyant effect of flood waters or saturated soil.

The primary advantage of lifting the house without the slab is that the house is lighter and therefore easier to lift. This benefit applies mainly to frame and masonry veneer houses. This method has several disadvantages, however:

- Cutting holes in the interior and exterior walls of the house and attaching wood bracing causes extensive damage that must be repaired before the elevated house is habitable.

- Because of the damage to the habitable parts of the house, alternative housing may be needed for an extended period.

- The contents of the house must be removed before the elevation process can begin.

- Masonry veneer is likely to interfere with the installation of exterior wall bracing and to crack or break off if left in place during elevation.

Because of these disadvantages, lifting a slab-on-grade house without the slab is normally done only when the house has been severely damaged by a flood or other event and would require extensive repairs regardless of the elevation method used.

Alternative Elevation Techniques for Masonry Houses on Slab-on-Grade Foundations

PROCESS:
Elevating by Extending the Walls of the House

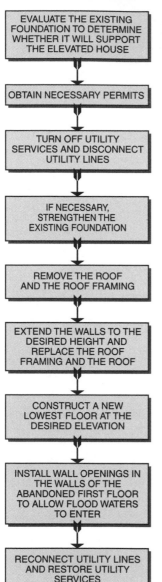

EVALUATE THE EXISTING FOUNDATION TO DETERMINE WHETHER IT WILL SUPPORT THE ELEVATED HOUSE
OBTAIN NECESSARY PERMITS
TURN OFF UTILITY SERVICES AND DISCONNECT UTILITY LINES
IF NECESSARY, STRENGTHEN THE EXISTING FOUNDATION
REMOVE THE ROOF AND THE ROOF FRAMING
EXTEND THE WALLS TO THE DESIRED HEIGHT AND REPLACE THE ROOF FRAMING AND THE ROOF
CONSTRUCT A NEW LOWEST FLOOR AT THE DESIRED ELEVATION
INSTALL WALL OPENINGS IN THE WALLS OF THE ABANDONED FIRST FLOOR TO ALLOW FLOOD WATERS TO ENTER
RECONNECT UTILITY LINES AND RESTORE UTILITY SERVICES

Elevating by Extending the Walls of the House

An alternative technique for elevating a masonry house on a slab-on-grade foundation is to extend the existing walls of the house upward and then build a new elevated floor above the old slab. This technique is Illustrated in Figures 5-9a through 5-9c.

First the roof and roof framing are removed so that the tops of the walls will be accessible. The contractor can then extend the walls upward with additional courses of either concrete block (as shown in Figure 5-9b) or brick or with wood or metal framing. The choice of materials is based on several considerations, including cost, the final appearance of the house, the strength of the existing foundation, and the design requirements associated with the identified hazards, including high winds and earthquakes.

The final height of the extended walls will usually depend on how high the lowest floor must be elevated. For example if the lowest floor must be elevated 3 feet to reach the FPE, the height of the walls must be increased by the same amount if the original ceiling heights in the house are to be maintained.

The new lowest floor can be either a wood-framed floor system or an elevated concrete slab similar to the original slab. When a new wood-framed floor system is installed, the area below the floor becomes a crawlspace (as in Figure 5-9c) or other enclosed area that may be used for parking, storage, or building access. So openings must be installed in the foundation walls to allow external and internal water pressures to equalize. Additional wall openings may be needed for ventilation.

For a new elevated slab floor, fill dirt is placed on top of the old slab and compacted as required. Then a new slab is poured on top of the fill. When this method is used, openings in the foundation walls are not required, because the entire area under the new slab is completely filled with dirt and is therefore protected from the pressure of flood waters.

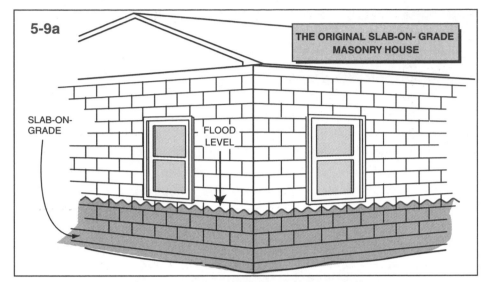

5-9a

THE ORIGINAL SLAB-ON- GRADE MASONRY HOUSE

SLAB-ON-GRADE

FLOOD LEVEL

Figures 5-9a through 5-9c. Extending the walls of a solid masonry house.

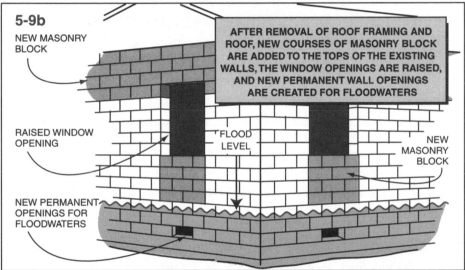

5-9b

NEW MASONRY BLOCK

AFTER REMOVAL OF ROOF FRAMING AND ROOF, NEW COURSES OF MASONRY BLOCK ARE ADDED TO THE TOPS OF THE EXISTING WALLS, THE WINDOW OPENINGS ARE RAISED, AND NEW PERMANENT WALL OPENINGS ARE CREATED FOR FLOODWATERS

RAISED WINDOW OPENING

FLOOD LEVEL

NEW MASONRY BLOCK

NEW PERMANENT OPENINGS FOR FLOODWATERS

NOTE

For more information about openings require-ments, refer to FEMA Technical Bulletin 1-93, *Openings in Foundation Walls for Buildings Lo-cated in Special Flood Hazard Areas, and FEMA 259, Engineering Principles and Practices for Retrofitting Flood Prone Residential Buildings.*

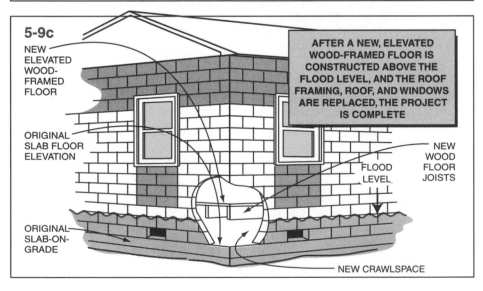

5-9c

NEW ELEVATED WOOD-FRAMED FLOOR

AFTER A NEW, ELEVATED WOOD-FRAMED FLOOR IS CONSTRUCTED ABOVE THE FLOOD LEVEL, AND THE ROOF FRAMING, ROOF, AND WINDOWS ARE REPLACED, THE PROJECT IS COMPLETE

ORIGINAL SLAB FLOOR ELEVATION

NEW WOOD FLOOR JOISTS

FLOOD LEVEL

ORIGINAL SLAB-ON-GRADE

NEW CRAWLSPACE

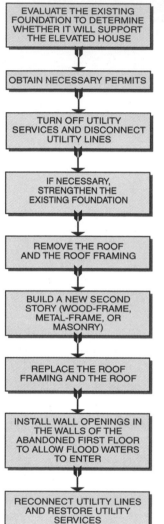

PROCESS:
Elevating by Abandoning the Lower Enclosed Area and Building a New Second-Story Living Area

EVALUATE THE EXISTING FOUNDATION TO DETERMINE WHETHER IT WILL SUPPORT THE ELEVATED HOUSE

OBTAIN NECESSARY PERMITS

TURN OFF UTILITY SERVICES AND DISCONNECT UTILITY LINES

IF NECESSARY, STRENGTHEN THE EXISTING FOUNDATION

REMOVE THE ROOF AND THE ROOF FRAMING

BUILD A NEW SECOND STORY (WOOD-FRAME, METAL-FRAME, OR MASONRY)

REPLACE THE ROOF FRAMING AND THE ROOF

INSTALL WALL OPENINGS IN THE WALLS OF THE ABANDONED FIRST FLOOR TO ALLOW FLOOD WATERS TO ENTER

RECONNECT UTILITY LINES AND RESTORE UTILITY SERVICES

Elevating by Abandoning the Lower Enclosed Area

Another alternative for a masonry house on a slab-on-grade foundation is to abandon the existing lower enclosed area of the house (the area with the slab floor) and allow it to remain below the FPE. This technique requires that the living area be restricted to upper floors of the house and that the lower enclosed area be used only for parking, storage, and access. Because this technique leaves the original floor and walls below the FPE exposed to flooding, it is best suited to masonry houses on slab-on-grade foundations. In these houses both the walls and floor are made of concrete or masonry, which are not easily damaged by contact with flood waters.

The amount of work required for this technique depends largely on whether the house already has an upper floor that can be used for living space. When an upper floor exists, abandoning the lower enclosed area involves removing easily damaged interior finishing materials below the FPE (including interior wall sheathing and insulation) and elevating or relocating vulnerable appliances (such as furnaces, washing machines, and freezers) and utility system components (such as electrical wiring and service boxes). These modifications are the same as those required for wet floodproofing, as described in Chapter 6. Refer to that chapter for details.

For one-story houses, abandoning the lower enclosed area requires the construction of a new second story as shown in Figures 5-10a through 5-10c. The required steps are similar to those described in the previous section, *Elevating by Extending the Walls of the House*. The roof and roof framing are removed, a new second story is built on top of the existing walls, the roof and roof framing are replaced, and openings are added for floodwaters. The construction options are the same: frame or masonry. Again, the choice is based primarily on the considerations of cost, final appearance, the strength of the existing foundation, and the need to address other natural hazards, such as high winds and earthquakes.

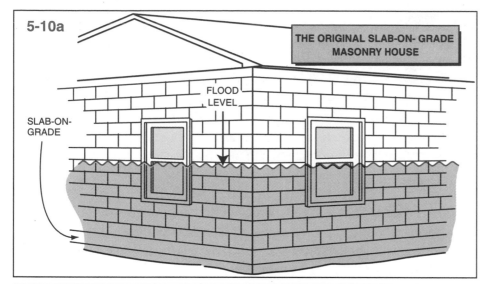

5-10a

THE ORIGINAL SLAB-ON- GRADE MASONRY HOUSE

FLOOD LEVEL

SLAB-ON-GRADE

Figures 5-10a through 5-10c. Adding a new second story over an abandoned lowest floor.

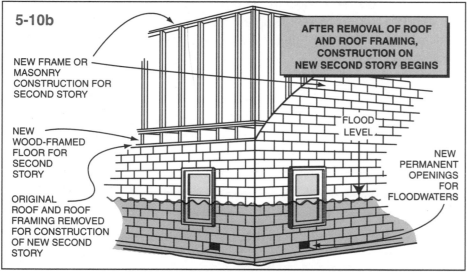

5-10b

AFTER REMOVAL OF ROOF AND ROOF FRAMING, CONSTRUCTION ON NEW SECOND STORY BEGINS

NEW FRAME OR MASONRY CONSTRUCTION FOR SECOND STORY

NEW WOOD-FRAMED FLOOR FOR SECOND STORY

ORIGINAL ROOF AND ROOF FRAMING REMOVED FOR CONSTRUCTION OF NEW SECOND STORY

FLOOD LEVEL

NEW PERMANENT OPENINGS FOR FLOODWATERS

NOTE

For more information about openings requirements, refer to FEMA Technical Bulletin 1-93, *Openings in Foundation Walls for Buildings Located in Special Flood Hazard Areas*, and FEMA 259, *Engineering Principles and Practices for Retrofitting Flood Prone Residential Buildings.*

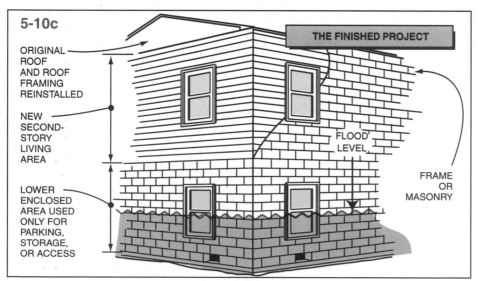

5-10c

THE FINISHED PROJECT

ORIGINAL ROOF AND ROOF FRAMING REINSTALLED

NEW SECOND-STORY LIVING AREA

LOWER ENCLOSED AREA USED ONLY FOR PARKING, STORAGE, OR ACCESS

FLOOD LEVEL

FRAME OR MASONRY

PROCESS:
Elevating on Piers

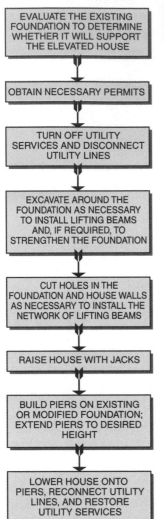

EVALUATE THE EXISTING FOUNDATION TO DETERMINE WHETHER IT WILL SUPPORT THE ELEVATED HOUSE

OBTAIN NECESSARY PERMITS

TURN OFF UTILITY SERVICES AND DISCONNECT UTILITY LINES

EXCAVATE AROUND THE FOUNDATION AS NECESSARY TO INSTALL LIFTING BEAMS AND, IF REQUIRED, TO STRENGTHEN THE FOUNDATION

CUT HOLES IN THE FOUNDATION AND HOUSE WALLS AS NECESSARY TO INSTALL THE NETWORK OF LIFTING BEAMS

RAISE HOUSE WITH JACKS

BUILD PIERS ON EXISTING OR MODIFIED FOUNDATION; EXTEND PIERS TO DESIRED HEIGHT

LOWER HOUSE ONTO PIERS, RECONNECT UTILITY LINES, AND RESTORE UTILITY SERVICES

NOTE

Elevating on an open foundation is an appropriate retrofitting technique for houses in Coastal High Hazard Areas (Zones V, VE, or V1-V30 on a FIRM).

Elevating on an Open Foundation

Frame, masonry veneer, and masonry houses on basement, crawlspace, and slab-on-grade foundations can also be elevated on open foundations consisting of piers, posts, columns, or pilings. Houses originally constructed on open foundations can also be elevated this way.

Piers

Figures 5-11a through 5-11d show how a house on a basement or crawlspace foundation can be elevated on masonry piers. The lifting process is the same as that shown in Figure 5-4 for elevating on extended foundation walls. Once the house is lifted high enough, new masonry piers are built on the existing foundation, if it is adequate. If the existing foundation is not adequate to support the elevated house, it will have to be either modified or removed and replaced by separate footings for the individual piers.

An existing basement would have to be filled in with dirt and graded. An old basement slab would usually be left in place and covered with fill dirt. But the slab would be broken up so that it would not be forced up by the buoyancy effect of flood waters. The house in Figure 5-11d, has been elevated approximately one full story, and a new concrete slab has been poured at ground level below it. The open area below the house can be used for parking, storage, and access.

Piers can be constructed of cast-in-place concrete as well as masonry block. However, regardless of the construction materials used, piers are designed primarily for vertical loading imposed by the weight of the house, including its contents and any exterior loads such as those imposed by snow. Because the forces associated with flooding, wind, and earthquakes can impose horizontal loads, piers used in retrofitting must be adequately reinforced with steel bars. The connections between the piers and the original foundation and elevated house also must be able to resist the expected horizontal and vertical loads on the house.

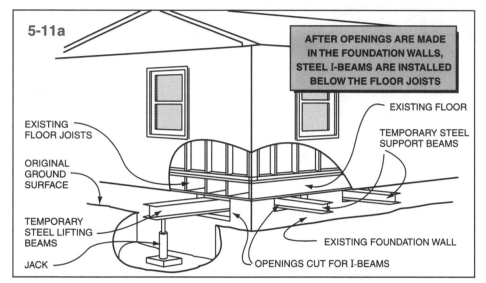

5-11a

AFTER OPENINGS ARE MADE
IN THE FOUNDATION WALLS,
STEEL I-BEAMS ARE INSTALLED
BELOW THE FLOOR JOISTS

EXISTING FLOOR

EXISTING
FLOOR JOISTS

TEMPORARY STEEL
SUPPORT BEAMS

ORIGINAL
GROUND
SURFACE

TEMPORARY
STEEL LIFTING
BEAMS

EXISTING FOUNDATION WALL

JACK

OPENINGS CUT FOR I-BEAMS

Figures 5-11a through 5-11d. Elevating a basement or crawlspace foundation house on piers.

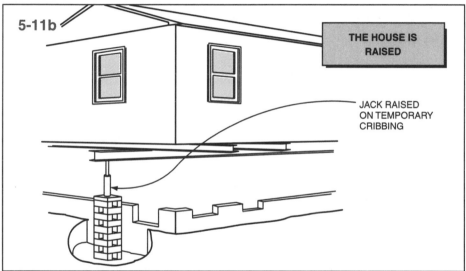

5-11b

THE HOUSE IS
RAISED

JACK RAISED
ON TEMPORARY
CRIBBING

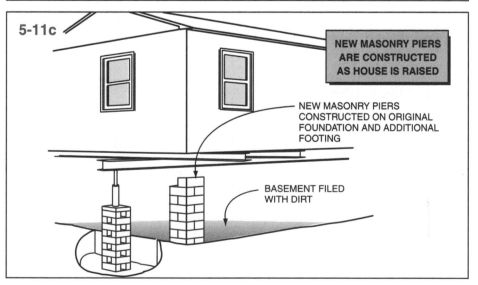

5-11c

NEW MASONRY PIERS
ARE CONSTRUCTED
AS HOUSE IS RAISED

NEW MASONRY PIERS
CONSTRUCTED ON ORIGINAL
FOUNDATION AND ADDITIONAL
FOOTING

BASEMENT FILED
WITH DIRT

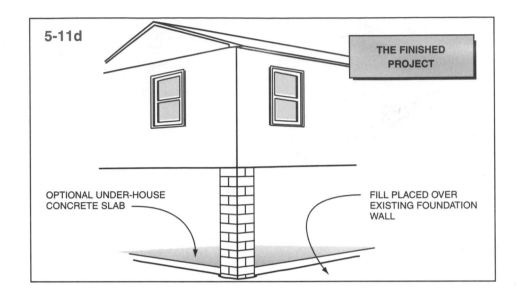

5-11d

THE FINISHED PROJECT

OPTIONAL UNDER-HOUSE CONCRETE SLAB

FILL PLACED OVER EXISTING FOUNDATION WALL

PROCESS:
Elevating on Posts or Columns

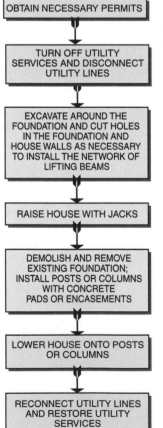

OBTAIN NECESSARY PERMITS

TURN OFF UTILITY SERVICES AND DISCONNECT UTILITY LINES

EXCAVATE AROUND THE FOUNDATION AND CUT HOLES IN THE FOUNDATION AND HOUSE WALLS AS NECESSARY TO INSTALL THE NETWORK OF LIFTING BEAMS

RAISE HOUSE WITH JACKS

DEMOLISH AND REMOVE EXISTING FOUNDATION; INSTALL POSTS OR COLUMNS WITH CONCRETE PADS OR ENCASEMENTS

LOWER HOUSE ONTO POSTS OR COLUMNS

RECONNECT UTILITY LINES AND RESTORE UTILITY SERVICES

Posts or Columns

Posts are usually placed in drilled or excavated holes. Each post or column is either encased in concrete or anchored to a concrete pad. The house elevation process is the same as that described for piers; however, the existing foundation must be removed so that the posts or columns and their concrete encasements or pads can be installed. Figure 5-12 shows a house elevated on two types of post or column foundations.

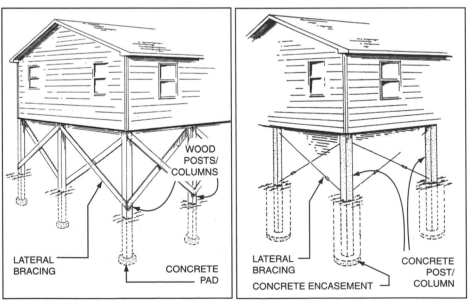

WOOD POSTS/ COLUMNS

LATERAL BRACING

CONCRETE PAD

LATERAL BRACING

CONCRETE ENCASEMENT

CONCRETE POST/ COLUMN

Figure 5-12   House elevated on posts.

Pilings

Elevating on pilings is a more involved process. Pilings are usually driven into the ground or jetted in with a high-pressure stream of water. They are not supported by concrete footings or pads. Unlike the construction of wall, pier, or post or column foundations, the pile driving operation, which requires bulky, heavy construction machinery, cannot be carried out under a house that has been lifted on jacks. Instead, the house is usually lifted and moved aside until the pilings have been installed. Because the existing foundation is not used, it must be removed. Figure 5-13 shows a house elevated on a piling foundation.

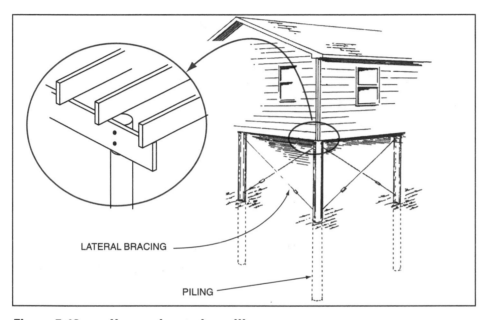

LATERAL BRACING

PILING

Figure 5-13　　House elevated on pilings.

PROCESS:
Elevating on Pilings

OBTAIN NECESSARY PERMITS

↓

TURN OFF UTILITY SERVICES AND DISCONNECT UTILITY LINES

↓

EXCAVATE AROUND THE FOUNDATION AND CUT HOLES IN THE FOUNDATION AND HOUSE WALLS AS NECESSARY TO INSTALL THE NETWORK OF LIFTING BEAMS

↓

RAISE HOUSE WITH JACKS AND MOVE IT OFF SITE TO A TEMPORARY LOCATION

↓

DEMOLISH AND REMOVE EXISTING FOUNDATION; INSTALL THE PILINGS

↓

MOVE THE HOUSE BACK TO THE SITE AND LOWER IT ONTO THE PILINGS

↓

RECONNECT UTILITY LINES AND RESTORE UTILITY SERVICES

Wet Floodproofing

Introduction

This guide describes two types of floodproofing: wet and dry. As its name implies, wet floodproofing allows flood waters to enter the enclosed areas of a house. In contrast, dry floodproofing (Chapter 7) prevents the entry of flood waters. The benefit of wet floodproofing is that if flood waters are allowed to enter the enclosed areas of the house and to quickly reach the same level as the flood waters outside, the effects of hydrostatic pressure, including buoyancy, are greatly reduced. As a result, the loads imposed on the house during a flood, and therefore the likelihood of structural damage, may be greatly reduced. Wet floodproofing is generally used to limit damages to enclosures below elevated buildings, walkout-on-grade basements, below-grade basements, crawlspaces, or attached garages. It is not practical for areas that are to be used as living space.

Successful wet floodproofing involves the following:

- ensuring that flood waters enter and exit the house

- ensuring that flood waters inside the house rise and fall at the same rate as flood waters outside

- protecting the areas of the house that are below the flood level from damage caused by contact with flood waters

- protecting **service equipment** inside and outside the house

- relocating any materials stored below the Flood Protection Elevation (FPE)

This chapter describes the modifications that must be made to a house as part of a wet floodproofing project, and it discusses the most important considerations regarding wet floodproofing. Protection of service equipment is discussed in Chapter 8.

WARNING

If your house has been substantially damaged or is being substantially improved, your community's floodplain management ordinance or law will restrict the use of wet floodproofing to attached garages and enclosed areas below the Base Flood Elevation (BFE) that are used solely for parking, storage, and access. For more information, refer to Federal Emergency Management Agency (FEMA) Technical Bulletin 7-93, *Wet Floodproofing Requirements for Structures Located in the Special Flood Hazard Area.*

DEFINITION

Service equipment includes utility systems, heating and cooling systems, and large appliances.

NOTE

Flood-resistant materials are discussed later in this chapter.

WARNING

If you are retrofitting a house that has been substantially damaged or is being substantially improved, your community's floodplain management ordinance or law will **not** allow you to have a basement, as defined under the NFIP. The NFIP regulations define a basement as "any area of the building having its floor subgrade on all sides." If your house has such a basement, you will be required to fill it in as part of any wet floodproofing project. Note that the NFIP definition of basement does not include what is typically referred to as a "walkout-on-grade" basement, whose floor would be at or above grade on at least one side.

Considerations

Flood Protection Elevation

All construction and finishing materials in the areas of the house that will be allowed to flood must be resistant to damage caused by direct, and possibly prolonged, contact with flood waters. Areas used for living space contain floor and wall coverings and other finishing materials, furniture, appliances, and other items that are easily damaged by flood waters and expensive to clean, repair, or replace. Therefore, wet floodproofing is practical only for portions of a house that are not used for living space, such as a basement as defined by the National Flood Insurance Program (NFIP) regulations, walkout-on-grade basement, crawlspace, or attached garage. As shown in Figure 6-1, the FPE (including freeboard) should be no higher than your lowest finished floor.

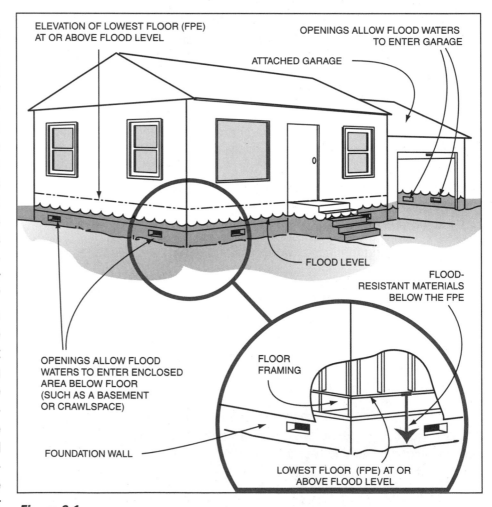

Figure 6-1
A typical wet floodproofed house that is compliant with the minimum requirements of a community's floodplain management ordinance or law.

If your FPE is above the elevation of your lowest finished floor, you should consider one or more of the other retrofitting methods described in this guide, such as elevation (Chapter 5). If you read Chapter 5, you will note that most of the elevation methods incorporate the principles of wet floodproofing. They raise the living space above the flood level and allow flood waters to enter the areas of the house below the living space.

Hazards

Wet floodproofing protects a house from the effects of hydrostatic pressure <u>but not from other flood hazards, such as the hydrodynamic force of flowing water, erosion and scour, the impact of ice and other floodborne debris, and damage from floodborne contaminants.</u> If you have seen evidence of these hazards in past floods in your area, or if your community officials confirm that your house may be affected by these hazards, you should consider an alternative retrofitting method, such as relocation (see Chapter 7) or elevation on an open foundation (see Chapter 5). Wet floodproofing a house does not change its vulnerability to damage from high winds or earthquakes.

Post-Flood Cleanup

Remember that flood waters are rarely clean. They usually carry sediment, debris, and even corrosive or hazardous materials such as solvents, oil, sewage, pesticides, fertilizers, and other chemicals. Allowing areas of a house to flood exposes those areas to whatever is in the flood waters. Cleaning up a wet floodproofed house after a flood may therefore involve not only removing mud but also washing, disinfecting, and decontaminating walls, floors, and other surfaces. This is another good reason why wet floodproofing is inappropriate for areas used as living space and, in some circumstances, why it may be inappropriate for <u>any</u> part of a house.

Modifications Required for Wet Floodproofing

Wet floodproofing requires a variety of modifications to your house, including its walls, construction and finishing materials, and service equipment.

Installing Openings

The most important part of a wet floodproofing project is installing wall openings that will allow the entry and exit of flood waters. The openings must be installed in foundation walls and in garage walls as appropriate, below the expected flood level (see Figure 6-1). The goal is not simply to allow the entry and exit of flood waters but also to ensure that the water

NOTE

For more information about openings requirements for wet floodproofing, refer to FEMA Technical Bulletin 1-93, *Openings in Foundation Walls for Buildings Located in Special Flood Hazard Areas*, and FEMA 259, *Engineering Principles and Practices for Retrofitting Flood Prone Residential Buildings.*

level inside the house rises and falls at roughly the same rate as the water level outside so that hydrostatic pressures inside and outside are continually equalized. As shown in Figure 6-2, large differences in the interior and exterior water levels allow unequalized hydrostatic pressures and therefore defeat the purpose of wet floodproofing.

Figure 6-2
Wall openings must allow flood waters not only to enter the house but also to rise and fall at the same rate as flood waters outside.

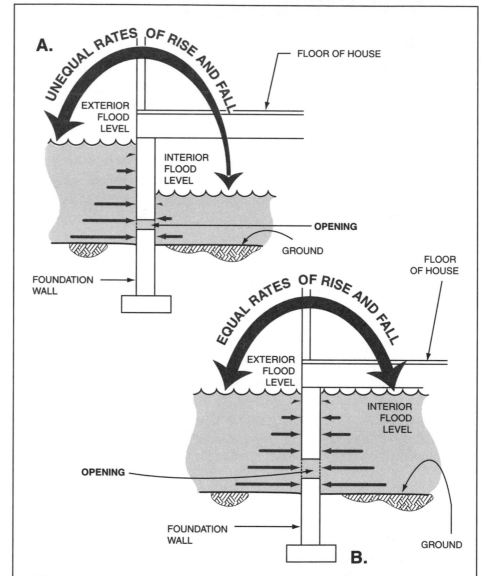

When the number and/or size of openings in foundation walls are inadequate (A), interior flood levels cannot rise or fall as fast as exterior flood levels. As a result, hydrostatic pressures, as indicated by the horizontal arrows, are not equalized. When the number and size of openings are adequate (B), interior and exterior flood levels rise and fall at the same rate and hydrostatic pressures are equalized.

For equal water levels to be maintained, both the size and number of openings must be adequate. Otherwise, when flood waters are rising and falling, water will not be able to flow into or out of the house fast enough. The number of openings required and their size will depend on the rate of rise and the rate of fall of the flood waters (see Chapter 2) and on the size of the area that is being allowed to flood. In general, the faster the rates of rise and fall and the larger the flooded area within the house, the larger the number and size of openings required.

If you are wet floodproofing areas below the BFE in a substantially damaged or substantially improved house, your community's floodplain management ordinance or law will require you to install openings in the exterior walls of all enclosed areas below the BFE. The minimum requirements are as follows:

- You must provide at least two wall openings for each enclosed area -- one in each of two different walls. In other words, you cannot put both openings in the same wall.

- If your house has more than one enclosed area, you must install openings in the <u>exterior walls of each enclosed area</u> so that flood waters can enter directly from the outside.

- The total area (size) of all openings for each enclosed area must be equal to at least 1 square inch for every square foot of floor space in the enclosed area. For example, if the enclosed area is 25 feet by 40 feet (1,000 square feet), the total area of the openings must be at least 1,000 square inches, or roughly 7 square feet. In this example, you could meet the size requirement by providing two 3 1/2-square-foot openings or several smaller openings whose total area equals 7 square feet.

- The bottom of each opening must be no higher than 1 foot above the ground directly below the opening.

- Flood waters must be able to flow in and out of enclosed areas automatically. If you place louvers, screens, or other types of covers over the openings (which many homeowners do to prevent animals from entering the enclosed areas) they must not block the flow of water. Because the need for human intervention reduces the reliability of wet floodproofing, you may not install any type of electrically, mechanically, or manually operated cover.

FEMA developed these requirements to provide homeowners with a straightforward means of determining where and how to install wall openings without the aid of an engineer or design professional. The

NOTE

If you cover wall openings with louvers or screens, keep in mind that the more restrictive they are the more likely they are to become clogged with debris during floods and to prevent the flow of water. Make sure that any screens or louvers you use will allow the passage of water that contains suspended sediment and other small debris. After flood waters have receded, screens and louvers must be cleaned of any other debris that may have accumulated.

requirements provide a margin of safety for wet floodproofed houses subject to flooding with rates of rise and fall as high as 5 feet per hour. If you wish to install openings that do not meet one or more of the requirements listed above, your design must be certified by a registered engineer or other licensed design professional and approved by your local officials. See FEMA's Technical Bulletin 1-93, *Openings in Foundation Walls for Buildings Located in Special Flood Hazard Areas*, for more information about openings requirements.

NOTE

For more information about flood-resistant materials, refer to FEMA Technical Bulletin 2-93, *Flood-Resistant Materials Requirements for Buildings Located in Special Flood Hazard Areas.* This bulletin includes a detailed list of common floor, wall, and ceiling materials categorized according to their applicability for use in areas subject to inundation by flood waters.

Using Flood-Resistant Materials

In the areas below the FPE, any construction and finishing materials that could be damaged by flood waters must be either removed or replaced with flood-resistant materials as required by your community's floodplain management ordinance or law. Vulnerable materials include drywall, blown-in and fiberglass batt insulation, carpeting, and non pressure-treated wood and plywood. Flood-resistant materials are those that can be inundated by flood waters with little or no damage. They include such materials as concrete, stone, masonry block, ceramic and clay tile, pressure-treated and naturally decay-resistant lumber, epoxy paints, and metal. In addition to resisting damage from flood waters, these materials are relatively easy to clean after flood waters have receded.

Protecting Service Equipment

When you wet floodproof a house, you must also protect the service equipment below the FPE, both inside and outside the house as required by your community's floodplain management ordinance or law. Service equipment includes utility lines, heating ventilation and cooling equipment, ductwork, hot water heaters, and large appliances. Chapter 8 describes a variety of methods you can use to protect interior and exterior service equipment.

Other Methods

Introduction

This chapter describes four alternatives to elevation (Chapter 5) and wet floodproofing (Chapter 6):

 Relocation

 Dry Floodproofing

 Levees and Floodwalls

 Demolition

These methods can be as effective as either elevation or wet floodproofing, but they are used less often because they are costly and more complex.

Relocation

 ### Introduction

Relocation – moving your house out of the flood hazard area – offers the greatest protection from flooding. It also can free you from anxiety about future floods and lower or even eliminate your insurance premiums. However, relocation usually is the most expensive of the retrofitting methods.

The relocation process involves lifting a house off its foundation, placing it on a heavy-duty flatbed trailer, hauling it to a new site outside the flood hazard area, and lowering it onto a new, conventional foundation. The process sounds straightforward, but a number of considerations require careful planning.

NOTE

For information about house relocation companies, contact the International Association of Structural Movers (ISM) at P.O. Box 1213, Elbridge, NY 13060, (315) 689-9498.

Relocation is sometimes used as an alternative to demolition (as described later in this chapter) when a house has been damaged. Instead of demolishing the house, the owner may be able to sell it for salvage to a contractor, who will then move the house to another site, renovate it, and sell it. Relocation can also occur after a community acquires a floodprone property from the owner. Instead of leaving the house to be demolished, the owner may decide to keep the house and move it to property outside the flood hazard area.

Considerations
Condition of House
For a house to be picked up and moved successfully, it must be structurally sound. All the structural members and their connections must be able to withstand the stresses imposed when the house is lifted and moved. Before the house is lifted, the house moving contractor must inspect it to verify its structural soundness. A house that is in poor condition, especially one that has been damaged by flooding, may need so much structural repair and bracing that relocation will not be practical.

House Size, Design, and Shape
In general, the types of houses that are the easiest to elevate (as discussed in Chapter 5) are also the easiest to relocate: single-story, wood-frame houses over a crawlspace or basement foundation, especially those with a simple rectangular shape. These houses are relatively light, and their foundation design allows the house moving contractor to install lifting equipment with relative ease. Multistory houses and solid masonry houses are the most difficult to relocate because their greater size and weight requires additional lifting equipment and makes them more difficult to stabilize during the move. Slab-on-grade foundations complicate the relocation process because they make the installation of lifting equipment more difficult.

The relocation process is also more complicated for houses with brick or stone veneer, which can crack and peel off when disturbed. It may be cheaper to remove the veneer before the house is moved and replace it once the house is on the new foundation at the new site. For the same reason, chimneys may need to be removed before the move and rebuilt afterwards. If they are to be moved with the house, they must be braced extensively.

Moving Route Between Old and New Sites
Restrictions along the route to the new site can complicate a relocation project, especially for large houses. Narrow roads, restrictive load capacities on roads and bridges, and low clearances under bridges and power lines can make it necessary to find an alternative route. When no practical alternatives are available, the house moving contractor may have to cut the house into sections (as shown in Figure 7-1), move them separately, and reassemble the house at the new site. Experienced house movers can make the cuts and reassemble the house in such a way that it will not appear to have ever been apart.

Figure 7-1
When a house is too large to be moved in one piece, it must be cut into sections that can be moved separately and then reassembled at the new site.

Disruption of Occupants

Among all the retrofitting methods, relocation is the most disruptive for the occupants of the house. Before the house can be lifted, all utility systems must be disconnected. The house becomes uninhabitable at this point, and you will not be able to move back in until the house has been installed at the new site and all utility systems reconnected. In the interim, you will need temporary lodgings and a place to store your furniture and other belongings.

The Relocation Process

The relocation process consists of more than lifting and moving the house. You must work with your contractor to select a new site for the house, and the contractor must plan the moving route, obtain the necessary permits, prepare the new site, and restore the old site.

Selecting the New Site

Selecting a new site for your relocated house is similar to selecting a site on which to build a new house. You need to consider the following:

Natural Hazards – Remember that the goal of relocating is to move your house to a site that will be safe from flooding and other natural hazards. Before buying new property, check with local officials about the flood, wind, and earthquake hazards at any new site you may be considering (see Chapter 4).

Utilities – Determine how difficult it will be to install new utility systems and to have utility lines extended to your new site. You need to consider

NOTE

See Chapter 4 for information about working with local officials regarding flood hazards and permitting requirements in your community.

WARNING

Regardless of the age of your house, you may be required by local regulations to bring it up to current code when you move it to a new site. This requirement could affect not only the house but also its utility systems. You should check with your local officials about such requirements before you decide to relocate.

electrical, gas, water and sewer, telephone, and cable TV services. Your community will probably require that your new utility systems meet current code requirements. Regardless of these requirements, you should consider upgrading one or more of your utility systems to provide more energy-efficient service.

Accessibility – Your new site must be accessible to the house movers and to the construction crews that will prepare the site and build the new foundation for your house. The more difficult it is for contractors to reach and work at your new site, the more expensive your relocation project is likely to be. If extensive grading and clearing are necessary for adequate access, some of the characteristics that made the site attractive to you may be diminished.

Another important consideration regarding accessibility the difficulty of moving the house to the new site. In determining the best route between the old and new sites, the moving contractor must anticipate potential problems. For example, the progress of the house may be impeded by narrow bridges and road cuts, bridges with low weight limits, low-hanging utility lines and traffic signals, low underpasses, tight turns, and road signs and fire hydrants.

The moving contractor should be responsible for coordinating any special services that may be required to deal with obstacles, such as raising traffic lights, relocating signs, and constructing temporary bridges. Utility lines can usually be raised temporarily during the move, but utility companies often charge for this service. Sometimes it may be more practical to avoid obstacles by choosing an overland (non-road) travel route.

Permitting

You or your moving contractor will have to obtain permits to move the house on public roads or other rights-of-way. These permits may be required by local governments, highway departments, and utility companies, not only in the jurisdiction from which your house is being moved, but also any jurisdiction the house will pass through. If the moving route crosses or affects private land, you may need to obtain the approval of the landowner.

Obtaining the necessary permits and approvals may be a lengthy and complex process, and you may find that the requirements vary from jurisdiction to jurisdiction and agency to agency. So it is extremely important that you, your design professional, and your moving contractor investigate the need for permits and approvals early in the relocation process.

You or your design professional should check with local officials to make sure that when your house is moved to the new site, it will conform to all zoning requirements and building codes in effect at the time of the relocation. The design professional should also determine the local design standards and permitting requirements that govern the development of your new site. All permits required for construction at the new site, for moving your house, and for restoring the old site after the house is moved should be obtained <u>before</u> the relocation project begins.

Preparing the New Site

Before the house is moved, the new foundation is designed and is usually partially constructed. The foundation will be completed after the house is brought to the site. Clearing, excavation, and grading are necessary to allow construction to begin and to ensure that the house can be maneuvered on the site. Also, utility lines must be brought into the site so that there will be no delay in connecting them to the house and making it habitable.

Lifting the House

In general, the steps required in lifting a house off its foundation are the same as those described in Chapter 5 for elevating a house on extended foundation walls. As described in Chapter 5, the steps for houses on basement and crawlspace foundations differ from those for houses on slab-on-grade foundations.

Houses on basement and crawlspace foundations are separated from their foundations and lifted on steel I-beams that pass through the foundation walls directly below the floor framing. The lifting is done with hydraulic jacks placed directly under the I-beams. The process for houses on slab-on-grade foundations is similar. However, because these houses are lifted with the concrete floor slab attached, the I-beams are inserted below the slab.

Moving the House

After the house is lifted, the moving contractor performs whatever grading and excavation are necessary to create a temporary roadway that will allow the house to be moved to the street. The area beneath the house must be leveled and compacted so that trailer wheel sets can be placed under the house (see Figure 7-2). The wheel sets and lifting beams form the trailer on which the house will be moved.

NOTE

The timing of the move may be critical in areas with heavy traffic during morning and evening rush hours. In these areas, houses are often moved late at night or early in the morning .

NOTE

Refer to Chapter 5 for a description of how houses on various types of foundations are lifted off their foundations.

Figure 7-2
Trailer wheel sets are placed beneath the lifting beams.

After the wheels are attached, a tractor or bulldozer tows the house to the street. As the house is being moved, workers continually block the wheels to prevent sudden movement. At the street, the house is stabilized, the trailer is attached to a truck, and the journey to the new site begins.

Figure 7-3
The journey to the new site begins.

At the new site, the moving contractor positions the house over the partially completed foundation and supports the house on cribbing so the trailer wheels can be removed. As in the house elevation process described in Chapter 5, the house is lifted on hydraulic jacks to the desired height and the foundation is completed below it (see Figure 7-4). The house is then lowered onto the foundation, all utilities are connected, and any necessary backfilling and landscaping is completed.

Figure 7-4
Once the house is
raised, the foundation
is completed.

NOTE

Many homeowners have sold or deeded abandoned floodprone properties to local municipalities for use as parkland or open space.

Restoring the Old Site

After the house is moved, the old site must be restored according to the requirements of local regulations. Restoring the site usually involves demolishing and removing the old foundation and any pavement, such as a driveway or patio; backfilling an old basement; removing all abandoned utility systems; grading to restore areas disturbed by demolition; and stabilizing the site with new vegetation. Permits are normally required for demolition, grading, and vegetative stabilization.

If your old site included a septic tank or fuel storage tank, you may have to meet the requirements of environmental regulations aimed at preventing contamination of the groundwater. Depending on the age and condition of the tank, you may be required to drain and remove it. If it is an underground tank, you may have to drain it and anchor it to prevent flotation. You may also be required to test the soil around an underground tank to determine whether leakage has occurred. As the homeowner, you will usually be responsible for cleaning contaminated soil if there has been any leakage from the tank. In this situation, you will need the services of a qualified geotechnical or environmental engineer.

Local utility companies or regulatory officials can inform you about requirements concerning capping, abandoning, or removing various utility system components.

WARNING

DEFINITION

Service equipment includes utility systems, heating and cooling systems, and large appliances.

NOTE

For additional information about dry floodproofing techniques, refer to Federal Emergency Management Agency (FEMA) Technical Bulletin 3-93, *Non-Residential Floodproofing – Requirements and Certification for Buildings Located in Special Flood Hazard Areas,* and FEMA 259, *Principles and Practices for Retrofitting Flood Prone Residential Buildings.*

Dry Floodproofing

Introduction

Dry floodproofing is completely sealing the exterior of a building to prevent the entry of flood waters. Unlike wet floodproofing (Chapter 6), which allows water to enter the house through wall openings, dry floodproofing seals all openings below the flood level and relies on the walls of the house to hold water out. Because the walls are exposed to flood waters and the pressures they exert, dry floodproofing is practical only for houses with walls constructed of flood-resistant materials and only where flood depths are low (no more than 2 to 3 feet). Successful dry floodproofing involves the following:

- sealing the exterior walls of the house
- covering openings below the flood level
- protecting the interior of the house from seepage
- protecting **service equipment** outside the house

The following sections discuss the most important considerations regarding dry floodproofing and describe the modifications that must be made to a house as part of a dry floodproofing project. Protection of service equipment is discussed in Chapter 8.

Considerations

Flood Depth

The primary consideration in dry floodproofing, and the one that imposes the greatest limitations on the application of this method, is the effect of hydrostatic pressure. Because dry floodproofing prevents water from entering the house, the external hydrostatic pressure exerted by flood waters is not countered by an equal force from water inside the house (see Chapter 2). This external pressure results in two significant problems: heavy unequalized loads on the walls of the house and buoyancy, or uplift force, which acts on the entire house.

When water builds up against a wall, it pushes laterally against the wall. As the depth of water increases, so does this force, as indicated by the arrows in Figure 7-5. Tests performed by the U.S. Army Corps of Engineers[1] have shown that, in general, the maximum allowable flood depth for masonry and masonry veneer walls is approximately 3 feet. In these tests, walls exposed to greater depths of water either collapsed or suffered serious structural damage.

[1] The test results are documented in the following reports published by the U. S. Army Corps of Engineers National Flood Proofing Committee: *Flood Proofing Tests – Tests of Materials and Systems for Flood Proofing Structures,* August 1988; *Systems and Materials to Prevent Floodwaters from Entering Buildings,* May 1985; *Structural Integrity of Brick-Veneer Buildings,* 1978; *Tests of Brick-Veneer Walls and Closures for Resistance to Floodwaters,* May 1978.

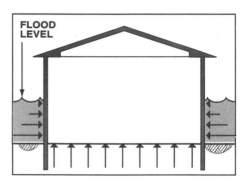

WARNING

Figure 7-5
The hydrostatic pressure exerted by flood water (including buoyancy) increases with depth.

No definitive testing has been carried out for conventional frame walls without masonry veneer. However, it is generally accepted that they are difficult to seal, weaker than masonry and masonry veneer walls, and likely to fail at lower depths.

Hydrostatic pressure is exerted not only by flood water but also by soils saturated by floodwaters. As a result, basement walls can be subjected to pressures much greater than that from 3 feet of water alone (see Figure 7-6). These pressures can easily cause basement walls to buckle inward or collapse (see Figure 2-8 in Chapter 2). <u>For this reason, your community's floodplain management ordinance or law does not allow basements in substantially damaged or substantially improved houses to be dry floodproofed. In fact, these basements must be filled in.</u>

The flood depth limits discussed here are provided as general guidelines only. Before you attempt to dry floodproof your house, a design professional, such as a structural engineer, must inspect it to determine whether it is structurally sound.

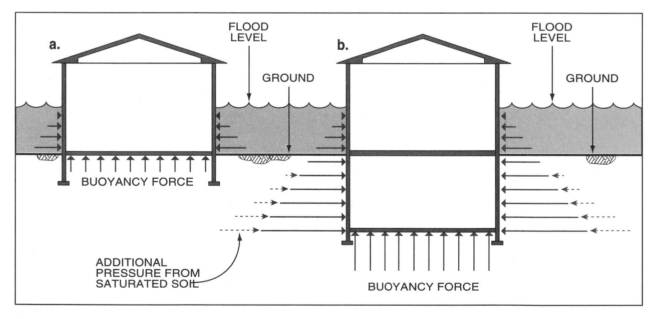

Figure 7-6
The lateral pressure resulting from the same depth of flooding is much less on the house without a basement (a) than on the house with a basement (b). The pressure on basement walls is caused by water and by saturated soils.

As shown in Figure 7-6, water and saturated soils also push up from below the house. This buoyancy force causes additional problems and creates a potential for damage that underscores the need to restrict dry floodproofing to areas where flood depths are low and to prohibit dry floodproofed basements. The buoyancy force resulting from flood depths of over 3 feet can separate a dry floodproofed house from its foundation and buckle concrete slab floors in dry floodproofed slab-on-grade houses. It may be difficult to imagine, but it is possible for a house with a dry floodproofed basement to be pushed out of the ground during large floods.

The degree of danger posed by buoyancy depends on the flood depth, the type of soil at the house site, how saturated the soil is, the duration of the flood, whether the house has a drainage collection and disposal system, and how well that system works.

Flow Velocity, Erosion and Scour, Debris Impact, and Wave Action
<u>Dry floodproofing does not protect a house from the hydrodynamic force of flowing water, erosion and scour, the impact of ice and other floodborne debris, or wave action.</u> If your house is in an area subject to any of these hazards you should consider an alternative retrofitting method, such as elevation on an open foundation (see Chapter 5), relocation (this chapter), or demolition (this chapter). Dry floodproofing a house does not normally change its vulnerability to damage from high winds or earthquakes.

Flood Duration
Flood duration is an important consideration because the potential for seepage through and deterioration of the materials used to seal the house increases with the length of time that the house is exposed to flooding. Also, the longer the duration, the greater the likelihood that the soil beneath and adjacent to the house will become fully saturated and add to the loads on the walls and floor (see Figure 7-6). If your house is in an area where flood waters remain high for days, weeks, or even months at a time, you should consider an alternative retrofitting method, such as elevation or relocation.

Human Intervention
Dry floodproofing systems almost always include components that have to be installed or activated each time flooding threatens. One example is a flood shield placed across a doorway. For this reason, dry floodproofing is not an appropriate retrofitting method in areas where there is little or no flood warning or where, for any other reason, the homeowner will not be able or willing to install shields or other components before flood waters arrive.

Post-Flood Cleanup

Remember that flood waters are rarely clean. They usually carry sediment, debris, and even corrosive or hazardous materials such as solvents, oil, sewage, pesticides, fertilizers, and other chemicals. The walls of a dry floodproofed house will be exposed to whatever is in the flood waters. Cleaning up a dry floodproofed house after a flood may therefore involve not only removing mud and debris from around the house but also decontaminating or disinfecting walls and other exterior surfaces.

Modifications Required for Dry Floodproofing

Dry floodproofing involves the use of sealants and shields, installation of a drainage system, and protection of service equipment.

Sealants

Except for some types of high-quality concrete, most wall materials are not impervious to water. Therefore, sealants must be applied to the walls of a dry floodproofed house to prevent leakage. Flexible sealants are compounds (such as asphalt coatings) or materials (such as polyethylene film) that are applied directly to the outside surface of the house walls. Sealants must also be applied to all structural joints, such as the joint between the walls and a slab floor, and to any other openings below the flood level, such as those where utility lines enter the house through the walls or floor.

Sealants that can be applied to outside walls include cement- and asphalt-based coatings and clear coatings such as epoxies and polyurethanes. Cement- and asphalt-based coatings are often the most effective, but they can drastically change the appearance of the wall (see Figure 7-7). For example, the aesthetic advantage of a brick wall is lost when these coating are used. Clear coatings do not change the appearance of the wall but are less effective.

Figure 7-7
a 12-inch-high asphalt coating was added to this brick wall.

Figure 7-8, a cross-section view of an exterior wall, shows one method of sealing masonry walls with an asphalt-based coating that does not detract from their appearance. In this method, a new masonry veneer is added to the existing veneer after the coating is applied. In addition to maintaining the look of the wall, the new veneer helps protect the wall against damage from floodborne debris.

Figure 7-8
New brick veneer added over asphalt coating.

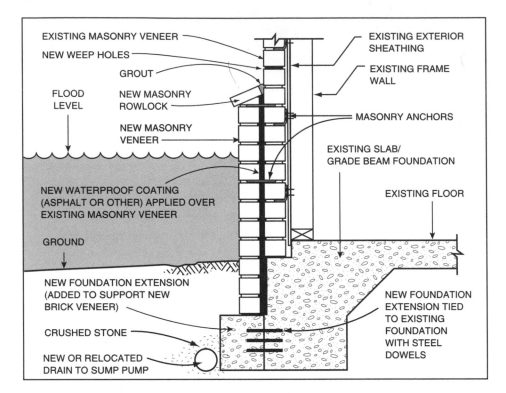

An alternative to using coatings is temporarily wrapping the entire lower part of the house in polyethylene film. This alternative is sometimes referred to as the "wrapped house" technique. The cross-section view in Figure 7-9 shows how this technique works.

Polyethylene film is not a strong material – it cannot withstand water pressure on its own and it can be punctured fairly easily. As a result, the following requirements must be met when the wrapped house technique is used:

- The installation must be carried out very carefully. Even a small hole in the film will leak under the pressure of flood waters.

- The film must be applied directly against the walls of the house so that the walls, rather than the film, provide the resistance to water pressures.

- Where the film covers doorways and other openings, it must be backed by framed plywood panels that have been braced to resist water pressures.

- A temporary drainage system must be provided that will collect and dispose of any water that leaks through holes in the film. (Drainage systems are discussed later in this section.)

- The duration of flooding should be less than 12 hours and the flood depth adjacent to the house should not exceed 1 foot.

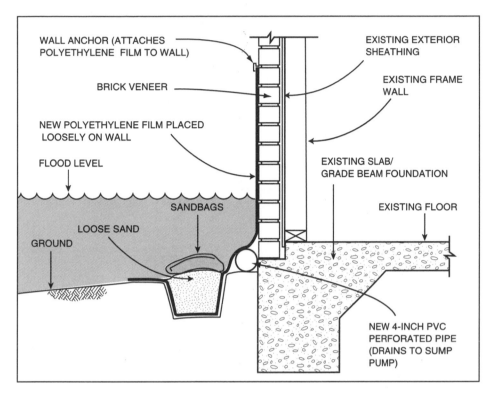

Figure 7-9
In the "wrapped house" method, the lower portion of the house is protected with a temporary layer of polyethylene film. As shown, a temporary drainage line is also required.

Because the wrapped house technique is only temporary, it does not change the normal appearance of your house. However, like any temporary technique, it requires extensive human intervention. All the necessary materials must be immediately available, and it will usually take four to six people several hours to put them into place. Therefore, you must have adequate warning every time flooding threatens so that you can install both the film and drainage system.

Commercial versions of the wrapped house technique are available. Usually, they consist of a system of vinyl-coated nylon wrapping mounted on rollers, which are contained in boxes permanently installed in the ground around the perimeter of the house. To protect the house, you open the boxes, pull the material out, and attach it to hooks or clips mounted on the walls of the house. The primary advantages of these commercial systems are that they provide a stronger barrier and allow for a shorter installation time. However, commercial house wrapping systems do not, by themselves, strengthen the walls of a house; if depths greater than 3 feet are expected, the walls must be adequately reinforced. Also, these systems do not eliminate the need for adequate drainage lines and sump pumps.

Shields

Shields are flood barriers placed over wall openings such as doorways and windows. Shields can be made of any of several materials, depending on the size of the opening to be covered. When flood depths are expected to reach the maximum allowable 2 to 3 feet, shields for openings wider than about 3 feet must be made of strong materials such as heavy-gage aluminum or steel plate (see Figure 7-10); shields for lesser depths and smaller openings can be made of lighter materials. For example, small windows can be protected with shields made of plywood .

Figure 7-10
Heavy-gage metal
shield over sliding
glass door opening.

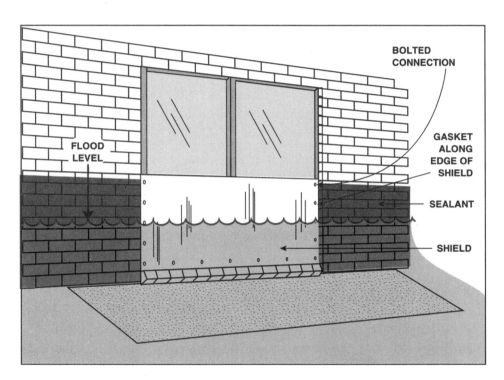

Because blocking all doors and other openings permanently would be impractical, shields are usually placed temporarily, after flood warnings are issued. Smaller, lighter shields can be stored in the house and, when needed, brought out and bolted in place or secured in permanently installed brackets or tracks (see Figure 7-11). Larger, heavier shields may have to be installed permanently on hinges or rollers so that they can be opened and closed easily.

Companies that specialize in flood protection devices can provide custom-fitted flood shields. Usually, these commercial shields are made of heavy-duty materials, and some are equipped with inflatable or other types of gaskets that help prevent leaks.

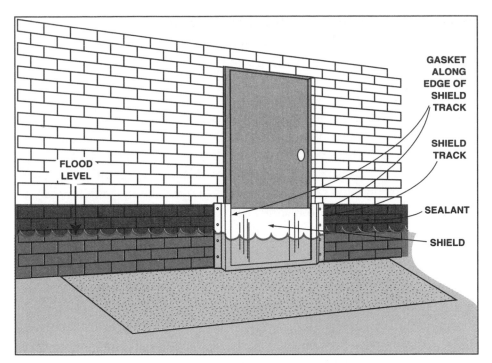

Figure 7-11
Light-gage metal shield held in place by permanently installed tracks.

GASKET ALONG EDGE OF SHIELD TRACK

SHIELD TRACK

SEALANT

SHIELD

FLOOD LEVEL

An alternative to using shields is to seal openings permanently. For example, a low-level window can be removed or raised and the opening bricked up or filled with glass block (see Figure 7-12). Placing fill dirt against the wall and extending the fill to a distance of at least 10 feet from the wall will provide additional protection from flood waters.

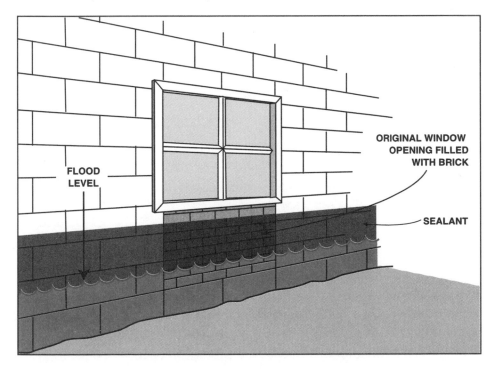

Figure 7-12
Low window raised approximately 2 feet and original opening filled with brick.

ORIGINAL WINDOW OPENING FILLED WITH BRICK

SEALANT

FLOOD LEVEL

Drainage Systems

Sealants and shields provide the bulk of the protection in dry floodproofing, but they may allow some leakage, especially during floods of longer duration and when damaged by debris. They also do not protect against "underseepage" – water that migrates downward along the sealed wall and then under the foundation. For these reasons, a dry floodproofed house must have a drainage system that will remove any water that enters the house through leaks in sealants and shields and any water that accumulates at the base of the foundation. Depending on the permeability of the soils around and under the house, the drainage system may have to be designed to reduce buoyancy forces also.

An adequate drainage system includes drains along the base of the foundation and under the floor. The drains consist of perforated pipe surrounded by crushed stone. The pipes collect water that seeps through the ground and channel it to a central collection point equipped with a sump pump. This system is shown in Figure 7-13. The sump pump must have sufficient capacity to handle the inflow of water and must have an emergency power source, such as a portable generator, so that it will continue to operate if conventional electric service is disrupted.

Figure 7-13
Drainage system for a
dry floodproofed house.

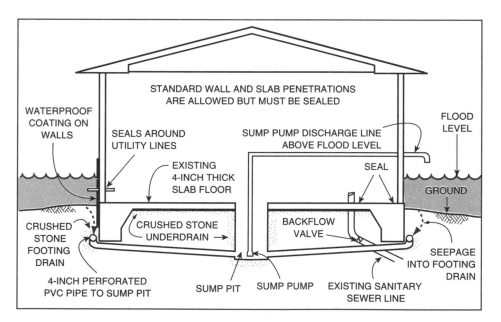

Protecting Service Equipment

Dry floodproofing a house will not protect service equipment outside the house. Examples of service equipment normally found outside the house are utility lines, air conditioning compressors, heat pumps, and fuel storage tanks. Chapter 8 discusses the protection of service equipment.

Levees and Floodwalls

Introduction

Levees and floodwalls are both barriers that hold back flood waters, but they differ in their design and construction, appearance, and application. Levees are embankments of compacted soil. They usually have rounded outlines and can be blended into the natural landscape of the house site. Floodwalls are structures built of manmade materials, such as concrete and masonry. Although they cannot be made to look like a natural landscape feature, they can be designed and constructed in such a way that they complement the appearance of the house and its site.

A levee requires more land area than a floodwall of comparable height; therefore, levees are less practical than floodwalls for small lots. Floodwalls, because of their design, construction, and more efficient use of space, not only can be built on smaller lots but also can be used selectively in conjunction with other retrofitting methods. For example, you can build a small exterior floodwall to protect an individual window or door in the wall of a dry floodproofed house. You can protect a walkout-on-grade basement by building a floodwall that ties into the ground where the grade rises above the flood elevation on the sides of the house. This approach is illustrated in Chapter 3, in the sample cost estimate for levees and floodwalls. You can also build an interior floodwall to protect service equipment in the basement of a wet floodproofed house (see Chapter 8).

Considerations

Levee or Floodwall Height

The height of your levee or floodwall will be determined partly by the Flood Protection Elevation (FPE) you have chosen. However (as explained in Chapter 3) height limitations imposed by design complexity, construction cost, and property space requirements, coupled with the need to provide at least 1 foot of freeboard, usually restrict the use of residential levees and floodwalls to areas where flood depths are no greater than 5 feet and 3 feet, respectively. If the flood depths at your house are greater, you should consider an alternative retrofitting method, such as elevation (Chapter 5), relocation (this chapter), or demolition (this chapter).

Remember that no matter what the height of a levee or floodwall, it can always be overtopped by a flood higher than expected. Overtopping allows water into the protected area, and the resulting damage to your house will probably be just as great as if it were not protected at all.

WARNING

Levees and floodwalls cannot be used to bring a substantially damaged or substantially improved house into compliance with the requirements of your community's floodplain management ordinance or law.

WARNING

Your community's floodplain management ordinance or law may prohibit the construction of levees and floodwalls in the regulatory floodplain and floodway. If you are unsure about your community's requirements or the location of your property in relation to the floodplain and floodway, check with your local officials. See Chapter 2 for information about the floodway.

WARNING

Because levees and floodwalls can increase flood hazards for other properties, you may find that local zoning regulations prohibit or restrict their use. Special permits may be required.

Overtopping is a bigger problem for a levee than a floodwall. Even a small amount of overtopping can erode the top of a levee and cause the levee to fail. When this occurs, large amounts of water may be released at once and cause even greater damage to your house. When flood waters threaten to overtop a levee, you may be able to raise the top of the levee temporarily with sandbags, but increasing the height of a levee increases the pressure of flood waters on it and may cause the levee to fail.

An important consideration for both levees and floodwalls is that they can give the homeowner a false sense of security. Every flood is different, and one that exceeds the height of your levee or floodwall can happen at any time. For this reason, you must not occupy your house during a flood.

Effect on Other Properties

A particularly important design consideration is the effect that a levee or floodwall can have on other properties. These barriers can divert flood waters away from your house and onto other properties. They can also impede or block flood flows. As a result, they can cause water to back up into previously flood-free areas or prevent natural surface drainage from other properties.

Levee and Floodwall Size

Levees are earthen structures that rely on their mass to resist the pressures of flood waters. To provide structural stability and resist erosion and scour, the sides of a levee are sloped – the width of the levee at its base is usually 6 to 8 times its height (see Figure 7-14a). As a result, the taller a levee is, the more space it requires. Most floodwalls do not rely solely on their mass for resistance to flood pressures. Therefore a floodwall will require less space than a levee of the same height, as shown in Figure 7-14b.

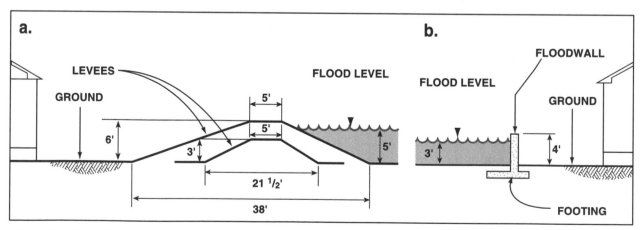

Figure 7-14   *Cross sections of a typical 3-foot-high levee, 6-foot-high levee, and 4-foot-high floodwall. A 4-foot-high floodwall (b) requires much less property space than a 3-foot-high levee (a).*

Soils

Most types of soils may be suitable for constructing residential levees. The exceptions are very wet, fine-grained, or highly organic soils. These soils are usually highly **permeable**. The best soils are those that have a high clay content, which makes them highly **impervious**. Using impervious soils for the levee and its foundation minimizes the seepage of water through or under the levee. Excessive seepage can weaken the levee and cause it to fail. If a sufficient amount of adequate soil is not available at the site of your house, the soil will have to be brought to the site or the levee design will become more complex. In either situation, the levee will be more expensive to build.

Soil type is an important consideration in floodwall construction as well. The soil under the floodwall, like that under a levee, must resist seepage. If the soils under a floodwall become saturated, the floodwall will no longer be adequately supported. As a result, the pressure of flood waters can cause it to lean or overturn.

Hydrostatic Pressure

Levees and floodwalls are designed to resist flood forces, but they may not be able to protect a house from hydrostatic pressure. The migration of moisture through the ground below a levee or floodwall, as a result of seepage or the natural capillary action of the soil, can cause the soil in the protected area to become saturated (see Figure 7-15). If this saturated soil is in contact with the foundation of the house, the resulting hydrostatic pressure can buckle slab floors, push houses up, and cause basement walls to bulge inward or collapse. If you plan to protect your house with a levee or floodwall, especially if you have a basement, your design professional should determine the potential hazard from hydrostatic pressure and take whatever steps may be necessary to protect against it.

DEFINITION

Permeable soils are those that water can easily penetrate and flow through. **Impervious** soils are the opposite. They resist penetration by water.

NOTE

You can usually get information about soil types from local officials, the agricultural extension services of state universities, and regional offices of the U. S. Natural Resources Conservation Service.

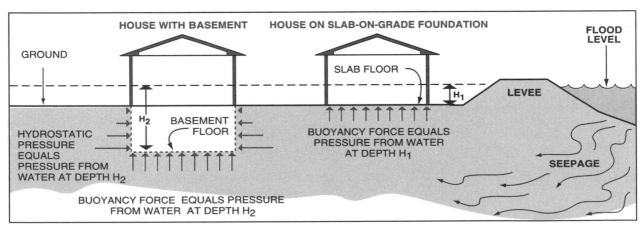

Figure 7-15   *Hydrostatic pressure in saturated soils poses a threat to houses behind levees, especially houses with basements. The amount of pressure depends largely on the level of the house in relation to the level of the water on the flooded side of the levee. The higher the water level is above the lowest floor of the house (as shown here by depths H_1 and H_2) the greater the pressure.*

WARNING

If your house has been substantially damaged or is being substantially improved, your community's floodplain management ordinance or law will not allow you to have a basement, as defined under the National Flood Insurance Program (NFIP). The NFIP regulations define a basement as "any area of a building having its floor subgrade on all sides." If your house has such a basement, you will be required to fill it in as part of any retrofitting project. Note that the NFIP definition of basement does not include what is typically referred to as a "walkout-on-grade" basement, whose floor would be at or above grade on at least one side.

Methods of reducing the risk of damage from hydrostatic pressure include moving the floodwall or levee further away from the house, installing a foundation drain system (drains and sump pump), and filling in basements with dirt.

Flood Conditions

Levees are most effective against floods that have low flow velocities and durations of no more than 3 to 4 days. High-velocity flows can scour or erode the sides of a levee and possibly cause it to collapse. Levees can be protected from erosion and scour in several ways. The sides of all levees should be stabilized with grass, which helps hold the soil in place. The sides of levees that will be subjected to higher-velocity flows can be armored with concrete or broken rock. Aligning a levee so that it is parallel to the flow of water will also help protect it from erosion and scour, and reducing the angle of the side slopes will make the sides more resistant to scour. Where the duration of flooding is expected to exceed 3 to 4 days, a levee may not be the most appropriate retrofitting measure. When levees are exposed to flood waters for prolonged periods, seepage and the problems associated with it are more likely to occur.

Access and Closures

As barriers, levees and floodwalls can block access to your house. If you build a levee or floodwall, you will usually need to provide openings or other means of access for driveways, sidewalks, and other entrances, but any opening in a floodwall or levee must be closed when flooding threatens. A variety of closure mechanisms are available. For floodwalls these include shields similar to those used in dry floodproofing (as described earlier in this chapter) that are hinged to the wall or designed to slide into place. Prefabricated panels stored elsewhere when not in use are also acceptable (see Figure 7-16). Acceptable closures for levees include permanently mounted, hinged or sliding flood gates and prefabricated stop logs or panels.

Figure 7-16
Slide-in closure panel.

An alternative to incorporating openings is to provide a means of crossing over the top of a levee or floodwall. If a levee is low enough, a ramp can be created with additional fill material. Similarly, a stairway can be built over a low floodwall, as shown in Figure 7-17.

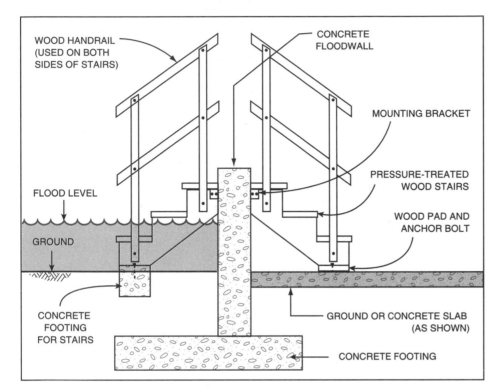

Figure 7-17
An access staircase over a low floodwall.

WARNING

Closure mechanisms require human intervention. Your levee or floodwall will not protect your house from flooding unless you are willing and able to operate all closure mechanisms before flood waters arrive.

Interior Drainage

Building a levee or floodwall around a house keeps flood water out of the protected area, but it can also keep water in – water that collects from rain or snow and from seepage during floods or, in the worst case, water that overtops the levee or floodwall. Two methods of removing this water should be used for all levees and floodwalls: drains and sump pumps. Drains installed at the base of a levee or floodwall allow collected water to flow out of the protected area. The outlets of the drains must be equipped with flap valves that close automatically during flooding to prevent flood water from backing up through the drains into the protected area.

An electric sump pump should be installed at the lowest point inside the protected area. The pump must have an adequate capacity – it must be able to remove water from the protected area faster than water enters. An emergency power source, such as a gasoline-powered generator, should be provided so that the pump will continue to operate during interruptions in electrical service, a common event during a flood. Whenever possible, the downspouts from the roof of the house should be directed over the levee or floodwall so that they will not contribute to the collection of water in the protected area.

Inspection and Maintenance
After a levee or floodwall is constructed, you must inspect it periodically and make whatever repairs are necessary. Otherwise, small problems, such as settlement, cracking, loss of vegetation, and minor amounts of erosion and scour, can quickly become major problems during a flood. At a minimum, you should perform these inspections each spring and fall, before each impending flood if you have adequate warning, and after each flood.

Protecting Service Equipment
Protecting a house with a levee or floodwall also protects any service equipment inside the house. Also, when levees and floodwalls protect not only the house but an area around it as well, service equipment mounted on exterior walls, such as an electric meter, and equipment installed near the house, such as an air conditioning compressor, will be protected. But any equipment outside the protected area must be relocated, elevated, or anchored. Chapter 8 discusses the protection of service equipment.

Levee Construction
The design professional must conduct an analysis of the soil at the site to determine whether it is adequate for use in the levee and to anticipate any foundation and seepage problems. When you construct a levee, you should try to take advantage of the natural terrain around your home. Depending on the topography of your lot, the levee may not have to completely encircle your house. You may be able to build the levee on lower ground and tie the ends into higher ground. An advantage of this technique is that the levee can often be made to look like part of the natural topography of your lot.

In preparation for construction, all ground vegetation and topsoil should be removed from the levee site. Sod should be set aside so that it can be used on the surface of the levee after construction. The levee should be built up in 6-inch layers, each of which must be compacted.

If there is a shortage of impervious soils in the area, the levee can be built with an impervious core and the available permeable soils can be used for the outer part of the levee, as shown in Figure 7-18. The core can be made of impervious soils or another type of water-resistant barrier. The core will minimize seepage through the levee; however, the use of permeable soils on the outside of the levee will require that the angle of the side slopes be reduced so that scour and erosion are minimized. This is an important consideration when property space is limited, because reducing the angle of the side slopes will increase the width of the levee base.

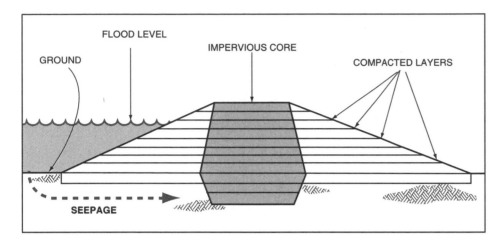

Figure 7-18
Levees are constructed with compacted layers of soil. When an adequate amount of impervious soil is not available, the levee can be constructed of permeable outer soils and an impervious core.

If the soil underlying the levee is highly permeable, an impervious barrier may have to be constructed below the levee to control foundation seepage. Several types of barrier designs are available, but they are normally used for major levee projects and would usually be too expensive for a homeowner. The analysis of the soil at the site will reveal such problems.

As noted earlier, the height of the levee will depend on the FPE and the need for at least 1 foot of freeboard. Also, the levee should be built at least 5 percent higher than the desired elevation. This additional height will compensate for settlement of the soil that occurs naturally after construction.

Floodwall Construction

The design professional must perform a soils analysis similar to that performed for levee construction. The purpose is to determine whether the soils will support the floodwall and whether seepage or migration or water through the soil will be a problem.

Construction, which begins with excavation for the foundation, varies according to the type of wall. The two main types of floodwalls are gravity walls and cantilever walls (see Figure 7-19). Both types resist overturning, which is the most common cause of floodwall failure, and displacement, but they do so in different ways.

The gravity floodwall relies on its weight and mass, particularly the mass at its base, for stability. The shear weight of the materials used in its construction (usually solid concrete, alone or in combination with masonry) make it too heavy to be overturned or displaced by flood forces.

NOTE

A reinforced cast-in-place wall with a foundation at the proper depth provides an excellent barrier to seepage because it is constructed of a single, solid, water-resistant material. The reinforcement not only gives the wall strength but helps it resist cracking.

Figure 7-19
Gravity and cantilever
floodwalls

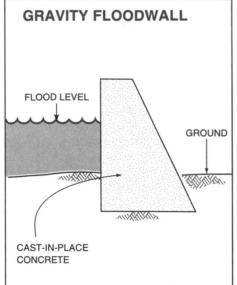

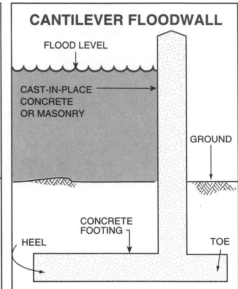

WARNING

Occasionally, flood-walls are built with a core of concrete block and a facing of brick. Even though the blocks are grouted, reinforced, and filled with concrete, experience has shown that this type of wall is neither as strong nor as resistant to leakage as cast-in-place concrete walls.

Gravity floodwalls are relatively easy to design and construct. However, the size of the wall increases significantly with height, so as flood depths increase, a cantilever floodwall becomes more practical.

A cantilever floodwall consists of a wall and footing constructed of cast-in-place concrete (similar to a foundation wall and footing for a house). The cantilever floodwall relies partly on the weight of the flood water and soil for stability. As shown in Figure 7-19, the "heel" of the wall (the portion of the footing on the flooded side) extends further than the "toe" (the portion of the footing on the protected side). Through leverage, the pressure of water and soil on the heel helps counteract the overturning force of the flood water. Reinforcement of a cantilever wall consists of steel bars embedded in the concrete.

Both masonry and cast-in-place cantilevered floodwalls can be faced with brick or stone or receive other decorative treatments that match or complement the exterior walls of a house (see Figure 7-20).

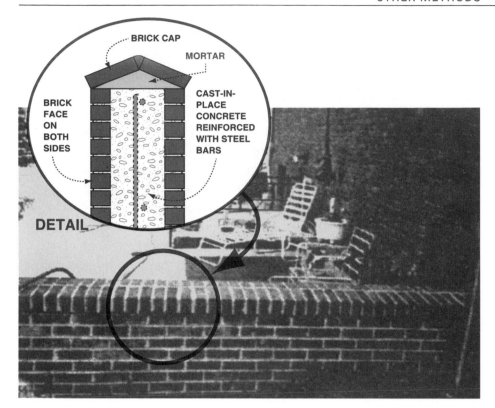

Figure 7-20
Typical brick-faced
concrete floodwall.
Detail shows cross
section through wall.

Demolition

Introduction

If a floodprone house has been severely damaged, because of flooding or any other cause, demolition can be a practical and effective retrofitting method. Demolition may also be practical for an undamaged house that, because of deterioration over time or for other reasons, is not worth retrofitting with any of the other methods described in this guide. If you choose the demolition method, you will tear down your damaged house and either rebuild properly on the same property or move elsewhere, outside the floodplain. Depending on your choice of a site for your new house, this method can lower or even eliminate your flood insurance premiums.

The demolition process involves disconnecting and capping utility lines at the damaged house, tearing the house down, removing debris and otherwise restoring the old site, and building or buying a new house. The most important considerations involve how badly your house has been damaged and your options for building or buying a new house.

NOTE

As discussed under *Financial Assistance for Retrofitting,* in Chapter 2, the cost of demolishing a substantially damaged house may be an eligible flood insurance claim under Increased Cost of Compliance (ICC) coverage.

Considerations

Amount of Damage

As a retrofitting method, demolition is more practical for severely damaged houses than for those with little or no damage. If a flood, fire, earthquake, hurricane, or other disaster has caused extensive damage to the interior and exterior of your house or left it structurally unsound, you will probably find that tearing the house down and starting over is easier than making all of the necessary repairs. Also, remember that a severely damaged house in the regulatory floodplain will almost surely be considered substantially damaged under your community's floodplain management ordinance or law. Salvaging such a house would require not only repairing the damage but also elevating (including filling in a basement); wet floodproofing areas used only for parking, storage, or access; or relocating the house as described elsewhere in this guide.

Rebuilding or Buying Another House

Tearing down a house is the easy part of the demolition process. You must also buy or build another house elsewhere or rebuild somewhere on your existing property. Regardless of your decision, your goal is to greatly reduce or eliminate the potential for damage from floods, earthquakes, high winds, and other hazards. If you buy or build a house elsewhere, you'll want to find a site that is outside the regulatory floodplain, ideally one that is well above the BFE. You should also consider the other hazards mentioned above. Check with your local officials about hazards in your community before you make your final decision.

When you buy or build a house elsewhere, you need to think about what you should do with your old property. Property that is entirely within the regulatory floodplain may be difficult to sell because of restrictions on its use. As explained in Chapter 2, some Federal programs provide grants to states and communities that they can use to buy floodprone houses and properties. State and local programs may also provide financial assistance. Check with your local officials about this.

When buying or building a house elsewhere is prohibitively expensive, you may be able to rebuild on your existing property, either on the site of your old house or, preferably, on a portion of your property that is outside the regulatory floodplain. If you rebuild on the site of your old house, your community's floodplain management ordinance or law will require that the lowest floor of your new house be at or above the Base Flood Elevation (BFE). You can meet this requirement by building the new house on extended foundation walls or an open foundation (as described in Chapter 5) or, in some situations, on compacted fill dirt. A important disadvantage of this approach is that you may not have access to your house during floods.

If your existing property includes a large enough area outside the regulatory floodplain, a better choice is to rebuild there. Building outside the floodplain gives you greater freedom to build the type of house you want. Also, because both the house and property are outside the floodplain, restricted access during flooding is less likely to be a problem.

Disruption of Occupants
Like relocation, demolition is very disruptive for the occupants of the house. Unless you decide to buy an existing house elsewhere, you must find a place to live and to store your furniture and belongings while your new house is being built.

Permitting
You or your design professional or contractor must check with local officials regarding permitting requirements for the necessary work. All permits for demolition, including disconnecting and capping utilities and disposing of debris; new construction; and restoration of the old site should be obtained before the demolition process begins.

The Demolition Process
Tearing Down the Old House
Your utility companies must first turn off all services to the house. Your demolition contractor will then disconnect the utility lines. If you do not plan to rebuild on the same site, the contractor will cap the lines permanently or remove them according to the requirements of the utility companies. Before demolition begins, environmental hazards, such as asbestos, must be abated in accordance with Federal, State, and local requirements. Usually, a demolition contractor will push the house down with a bulldozer and then dispose of the resulting debris as required by Federal, State, and local regulations.

Restoring the Old Site
If you are not rebuilding on the old site, it must be restored according to the requirements of local regulations. Site restoration usually involves demolishing and removing not only the house, but also any pavement, such as a driveway or patio; grading to restore areas disturbed by the demolition; and stabilizing the site with grass.

WARNING

If you rebuild on the site of your old house, your community's floodplain management ordinance of law will not allow you to have a basement.

If your old site included a septic tank or fuel storage tank, you may have to meet the requirements of environmental regulations aimed at preventing contamination of the groundwater. You may be required to drain and remove aboveground and underground tanks, or you may have to anchor them to resist flotation. You may also be required to test the soil around an underground tank to determine whether leakage has occurred. As the homeowner, you will usually be responsible for cleaning contaminated soil if there has been any leakage from the tank. In this situation, you will need the services of a qualified geotechnical or environmental engineering firm.

Local utility companies or regulatory officials can inform you about requirements concerning capping, abandoning, or removing various utility system components.

Rebuilding

Your construction contractor will prepare the site and build your new house according to the local building code and zoning requirements. If you are rebuilding on the original site, you must meet additional requirements of your community's floodplain management ordinance or law. Therefore, as noted previously, the lowest floor of your new house must be at or above the BFE, and you will not be allowed to build a house with a basement.

Depending on where you decide to rebuild, local utility companies may have to extend new lines into the site of your new house. Usually this is done before construction is completed. Your contractor will hook up the utility lines as part of construction. You may need the services of a design professional if specialized utility systems are required because of the location of your site, the type of house you decide to build, or the nature of the hazards at the site.

Protecting Service Equipment

Introduction

Houses are typically provided with a variety of building support service equipment, including the following:

- electrical systems (wiring, switches, outlets, fixtures, fuse and circuit breaker panels, meters)
- telephone and cable TV lines
- water and sewer lines and drains
- natural gas lines
- septic tanks
- heating, ventilating, and cooling (HVAC) equipment (air conditioning compressors, heat pumps, furnaces, ductwork, hot water heaters, fuel storage tanks)
- appliances (washing machines, dryers, freezers, refrigerators)

Some of this equipment is normally found inside the house, such as furnaces, ductwork, hot water heaters, and appliances; some is found outside, such as propane tanks, air conditioning and heat pump compressors, heat pumps, and septic tanks; and some includes components found in both locations, such as electrical systems; plumbing, gas, telephone, and cable TV lines; and oil storage tanks.

The original placement of service equipment in and around your house was probably based on standard construction practice and the economic concerns of the builder. As a result, in floodprone houses, service equipment is often installed in areas where it will be exposed to flood waters, such as in a basement or crawlspace or at ground level outside the house.

Elevation, wet floodproofing, and dry floodproofing protect the structure of your house from damage by flood waters. But these methods, unlike relocation and the construction of levees or floodwalls, do not prevent flood waters from reaching the house. For this reason, protecting service equipment below the expected flood level is an essential part of a retrofitting project.

NOTE

For more information about elevating electrical systems and heating, ventilating and cooling equipment, refer to the following Federal Emergency Management Agency (FEMA) Hazard Mitigation Fact Sheets: *Raise Electrical System Components* and *Raise or Floodproof HVAC Equipment.*

Methods of Protection

You can protect interior and exterior service equipment in several ways: by elevating it, relocating it, or protecting it in place.

Elevation

Service equipment installed outside your house can often be elevated above the flood level. Equipment mounted on an exterior wall, such as an electric meter and incoming electric, telephone, and cable TV lines, usually can be mounted higher up on the same wall. Equipment normally placed on the ground, such as heat pumps and air conditioning compressors, can be raised above the flood elevation on pedestals or platforms (see Figures 8-1 and 8-2).

When you elevate service equipment, you should always consider incorporating at least 1 foot of freeboard into your Flood Protection Elevation (FPE), just as you should when you protect your house with one of the methods described in this guide. Elevating service equipment an additional 1 or 2 feet often will not increase your retrofitting costs significantly.

The feasibility of elevating equipment inside a basement or garage will depend largely on the flood level. If the flood level is only 1 to 2 feet above the floor, large pieces of equipment such as furnaces, hot water heaters, and appliances can be elevated on platforms constructed of concrete or masonry block. As the height of the flood level above the floor increases,

Figure 8-1
An air conditioning/ heat pump compressor mounted on a brick pedestal outside an elevated house.

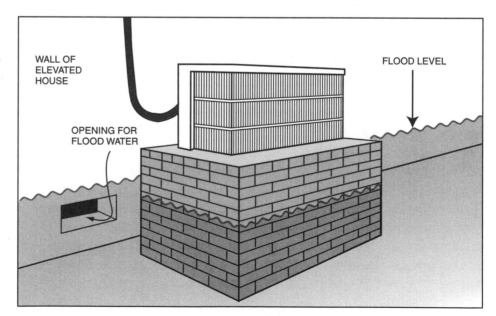

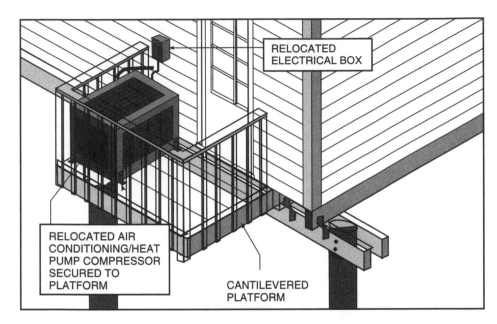

Figure 8-2
Air conditioning/ heat pump compressor mounted on a cantilevered platform attached to a house elevated on an open foundation.

RELOCATED ELECTRICAL BOX

RELOCATED AIR CONDITIONING/HEAT PUMP COMPRESSOR SECURED TO PLATFORM

CANTILEVERED PLATFORM

the amount of space available above the flood level diminishes and elevation will be feasible only for smaller pieces of equipment such as electrical system components, ventilation ductwork, or specialized equipment such as furnaces designed to be suspended from the ceiling. If the flood level is at or near the ceiling, elevation in lower areas will not be possible. Instead equipment will have to be relocated or protected in place as described in the following sections.

Keep in mind that most service equipment must remain accessible for routine maintenance. For example, your fuel company must be able to reach your fuel tank to fill or empty it. Before elevating any service equipment, your contractor should check with the utility company to find out whether it has any requirements that would prohibit elevation or restrict elevation height.

Also, remember that any large equipment elevated on platforms or pedestals, both inside and outside your house, may be more vulnerable to wind and earthquake damage. Before these elevation methods are used, a design professional must determine the expected wind and earthquake forces at the site and account for them in the design of the elevation method. This precaution is especially important for elevated fuel storage tanks, which could rupture if they were dislodged or toppled by wind and earthquake forces. In earthquake-prone areas, fuel storage tanks are sometimes equipped with cutoff valves that can help prevent leaks when supply lines are ruptured. Your utility service provider can give you more information about cutoff valves and other ways to protect fuel storage tanks from natural hazards.

Relocation

When space permits, you can move service equipment from a basement or other area below the flood level to an upper floor of the house or even an attic. Relocation will usually require more extensive changes to both your house and the equipment being moved, but it often provides a greater level of flood protection because the relocated equipment will be farther above the flood level. In some situations, you may also be able to relocate outside equipment to higher ground, but only when the slope of your lot and other site conditions permit.

Another relocation option is to build a new, elevated utility room as an addition to your house. The addition could be built on an open foundation or extended foundation walls.

Protection in Place

When elevation and relocation are infeasible or impractical, you can protect service equipment in place with low floodwalls and shields and with anchors and tiedowns that prevent flotation. Plumbing systems can be protected with valves that prevent wastewater from backing up into the house.

Floodwalls and Shields

Floodwalls and shields are normally components of dry floodproofing systems (Chapter 7) used to protect entire buildings. However, in wet floodproofing, they can be used for the protection of small areas within a building that contain service equipment that is not elevated or relocated. For example, a you can build a concrete floodwall that surrounds one or more pieces of service equipment, such as a furnace and hot water heater (see Figure 8-3).

If the expected depth of flooding is less than about 8 inches, the floodwall would be low enough that you could step over it to reach the protected equipment. A higher floodwall can include an opening equipped with a removable shield, as shown in Figure 8-3. The opening permits easy access to the protected equipment. In this example, the shield does not interfere with the normal operation of the equipment, so it should be left in place and removed only when necessary. Leaving the shield in place allows the barrier to function without human intervention.

In general, barriers and shields of the type shown in Figure 8-3 are practical only when flood depths are less than about 3 feet. The greater hydrostatic pressure exerted by deeper water requires barriers and shields that are more massive, have more complex designs, and are therefore more expensive. As discussed in Chapter 7, all floodwalls should provide at least 1 foot of freeboard above the expected flood elevation.

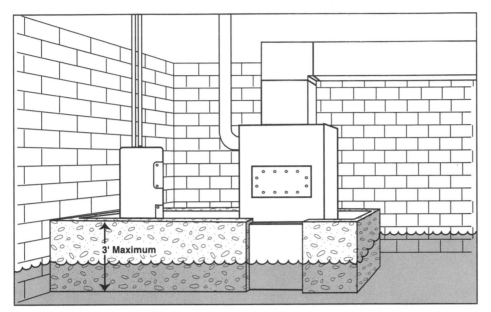

Figure 8-3
Hot water heater and furnace protected by a concrete floodwall with opening and shield.

3' Maximum

Regardless of the height of the barrier, the area it protects should be equipped with a sump pump that will remove any water that accumulates through seepage.

Anchors and Tiedowns

Anchors and tiedowns are used primarily for aboveground fuel storage tanks that are not elevated above the flood level and for belowground tanks. Both types are extremely vulnerable to flotation. Flood waters act directly on aboveground tanks; belowground tanks can be forced out of the ground by the buoyancy force of saturated soils. When either type of tank is displaced, its connections can be severed and the escaping fuel can cause hazardous conditions.

Aboveground tanks can be anchored with metal straps or cables that cross over the tank and connect to ground anchors. The length and type of ground anchor you need will depend largely on the type of soil at the site. A design professional can advise you about anchors. Another way to anchor an aboveground tank is to embed its legs in a concrete slab (see Figure 8-4).

Ground anchors can also be used for belowground tanks. This method involves excavating the soil above the tank, placing steel I-beams across it, and connecting them to ground anchors. Again, check with a design professional concerning the required size and type of anchor. Belowground tanks can also be anchored with a concrete slab similar to the one shown in Figure 8-4. Installing the slab, involves excavating around the tank and removing it temporarily while the slab is poured.

NOTE

For more information about anchoring fuel storage tanks, refer to the FEMA Mitigation Fact Sheet *Anchor Fuel Tanks*.

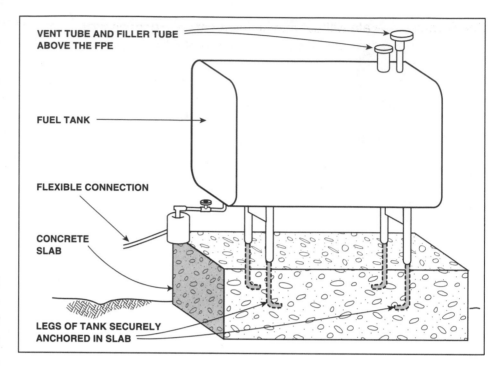

*Figure 8-4
Anchoring a fuel
storage tank with a
concrete slab.*

VENT TUBE AND FILLER TUBE
ABOVE THE FPE

FUEL TANK

FLEXIBLE CONNECTION

CONCRETE
SLAB

LEGS OF TANK SECURELY
ANCHORED IN SLAB

WARNING

Be especially careful when anchoring storage tanks or other service equipment in floodways, V zones, and other high-risk areas. You must consider the effects of high flow velocities, wave action, fast moving floodborne debris, and extensive erosion and scour wherever these hazards are likely to occur.

Another alternative is to excavate down to the tank and pour a concrete slab on top, making sure not to cover access openings.

On all tanks below the flood level, both aboveground and belowground, flexible connections must be used between the tank and the supply line. Also, the vent and filler tubes must extend above the FPE (see Figure 8-4). If you have adequate warning of an impending flood, top off the tank. A full tank will be less susceptible to corrosion from accumulated moisture and will be heavier and better able to resist buoyancy.

Although anchoring is particularly important for storage tanks, remember that the levels of future floods can exceed your FPE and inundate service equipment that you have elevated, relocated, or protected in place. For this reason, service equipment should be anchored whenever possible so that it will remain in place when acted on by flood forces.

Backflow Valves

Flooding can often inundate and overload sanitary sewer systems and combined sanitary/storm sewer systems. As a result, water can flow backward through sewer lines and out through toilets or drains. The best solution to this problem is usually to install a backflow valve. These valves include check valves, gate valves, and dual backflow valves.

Check valves operate without human intervention. Under normal conditions, they allow waste water to flow from the house to the main sewer line. When flooding causes the flow to reverse, a flap or other check mechanism in the valve prevents water from flowing back into the house. A disadvantage of check valves is that they can become blocked open by debris and fail to operate. For this reason, check valves must be inspected regularly and cleaned as necessary.

Gate valves are manually operated, provide a better seal, and are unlikely to be blocked open. However, they are more expensive than check valves and require human intervention.

The third alternative, dual backflow valves, combine the benefits of the check valve and the gate valve. As the most expensive of the three types, the dual backflow valve should be considered primarily for use in houses subject to repeated backflow flooding. Gate valves and dual backflow valves are usually installed outside the house in a valve pit (see Figure 8-5).

NOTE

The installation of backflow valves and other plumbing modifications is usually regulated by State and local building codes. A plumber or contractor licensed to work in your area will know about the code requirements that apply to your retrofitting project.

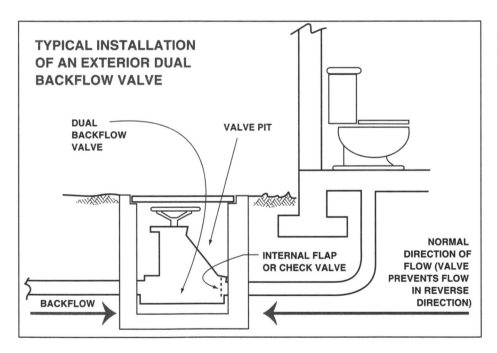

Figure 8-5
Dual backflow valve installed in exterior valve pit.

Appendix A

Bibliography and Sources of Information

FEMA and other organizations have produced many documents about floodproofing and flood hazard mitigation. Those listed below provide information that may be useful to a homeowner who is thinking about undertaking a retrofitting project.

American Society of Civil Engineers, *Minimum Design Loads for Buildings and Other Structures,* ASCE 7-95, 1996

Federal Emergency Management Agency
Protecting Your Home from Flood Damage, Mitigation Ideas for Reducing Flood Loss, 2nd Edition, revised 1996

Engineering Principles and Practices for Retrofitting Flood Prone Residential Buildings, FEMA 259, January 1995

Mitigation of Flood and Erosion Damage to Residential Buildings in Coastal Areas, FEMA 257, October 1994

Answers to Questions About Substantially Damaged Buildings, FEMA-213, May 1991

Floodproofing Non-Residential Structures, FEMA 102, May 1986

Coastal Construction Manual, FEMA 55, February 1986

Elevated Residential Structures, FEMA 54, March 1984

Federal Emergency Management Agency and the American Red Cross, *Repairing Your Flooded Home*, FEMA 234 and ARC 4477, August 1992

Federal Emergency Management Agency and the National Association of Home Builders, *Best Build 3: Protecting a Flood-Prone Home* (30-minute video)

Florida Department of Community Affairs, Division of Emergency Management, Bureau of Recovery and Mitigation, State Assistance Office for the NFIP, *Retrofitting and Flood Mitigation in Florida*, January 1995

Illinois Department of Transportation, Division of Water Resources
Flooded Basements: A Homeowner's Guide, August Edition, 1992

Flood Hazard Mitigation, May 1988

Protect Your Home from Flood Damage, January 1985

Elevating or Relocating a House to Reduce Flood Damage, Local Assistance Series 3C, revised 1986

Illinois Department of Transportation, Division of Water Resources, and University of Illinois, Small Homes Council – Building Research Council, *Elevating Flood-Prone Buildings: A Contractor's Guide*, Local Assistance Series 3D, undated

Nebraska Natural Resources Commission, Flood Plain Management Section, *Flood Preparedness and Response Handbook*, March 1984

University of Chicago, Center for Urban Studies, Introduction to Flood Proofing – An Outline of Principles and Methods, April 1967

U.S. Army Corps of Engineers
Flood-Proofing Regulations, EP 1165-2-314, December 15, 1995

A Flood Proofing Success Story Along Dry Creek at Goodlettsville, Tennessee, April 1995

Local Flood Proofing Programs, June 1994

Flood Proofing – How to Evaluate Your Options, July 1993

Flood Proofing Techniques, Programs, and References, February 1991

Raising and Moving a Slab-on-Grade House, 1990

Flood Proofing Tests, Tests of Materials and Systems for Flood Proofing Structures, August 1988

Flood Proofing Systems and Techniques, December 1984

For information about natural hazards and hazard mitigation, visit the Internet sites listed below:

American Red Cross
http://www.crossnet.org/

Applied Technology Council
http://www.atcouncil.org/

Association of State Floodplain Managers
http://www.floods.org

Disaster Research Center, University of Delaware
http://www.udel.edu/DRC/

Earthquake Hazards Mitigation Information Network
http://www.eqnet.org/index.html

Federal Emergency Management Agency
http://www.fema.gov

Hazard Reduction and Recovery Center (HRRC), Texas A&M
http://chud.tamu.edu/hrrc/hrrc-home.html

National Geophysical Data Center / WDC-A for Solid Earth Geophysics, Boulder, Colorado
http://www.ngdc.noaa.gov/seg/hazard/hazards.html

National Information Service for Earthquake Engineering, University of California at Berkeley
http://nisee.ce.berkeley.edu/

U. S. Geological Survey – Earthquake Hazards and Preparedness
http://quake.wr.usgs.gov/hazprep

Natural Hazards Center at the University of Colorado, Boulder, Colorado
http://www.colorado.edu/hazards/

U. S. Natural Resources Conservation Service
http://www.nrcs.usda.gov/

Wind Engineering Research Center, Texas Tech University
http:// www.ce.ttu.edu/wind/main.html

Appendix B

Glossary

Many of the terms defined here are also defined in the margins of pages on which they first appear or explained in the body of the text.

Active retrofitting method – Method that will not function as intended without human intervention. See "Passive retrofitting method."

Adjacent grade – See "Lowest Adjacent Grade (LAG)."

Alluvial fan flooding – Flooding that occurs on the surface of an alluvial fan (or similar landform) that originates at the apex of the fan and is characterized by high-velocity flows; active processes of erosion, sediment transport, and deposition; and unpredictable flow paths.

Armor – To protect fill slopes, such as the sides of a levee, by covering them with erosion-resistant materials such as rock or concrete.

Backfill – To fill in a hole with the soil removed from it or with other material, such as soil, gravel, or stone.

Backflow valve – see Check valve.

Base Flood – Flood that has a 1-percent probability of being equaled or exceeded in any given year. Also known as the 100-year flood.

Base Flood Elevation (BFE) – Elevation of the 100-year flood. This elevation is the basis of the insurance and floodplain management requirements of the National Flood Insurance Program.

Basement – As defined by the NFIP regulations, any area of a building having its floor subgrade on all sides.

Cast-in-place concrete – Concrete poured and formed at the construction site.

Check valve – Valve that allows water to flow in one direction but automatically closes when the direction of flow is reversed.

Closure – Shield made of strong material, such as metal or wood, used to temporarily close openings in levees, floodwalls, and dry floodproofed buildings.

Coastal High Hazard Area – Area of special flood hazard (designated Zone V, VE, or V1 - V30 on a FIRM) that extends from offshore to the inland limit of a primary frontal dune along an open coast, and any other area subject to high-velocity wave action from storms or seismic sources.

Compaction – In construction, the process by which the density of earth fill is increased so that it will provide a sound base for a building or other structure.

Crawlspace – Type of foundation in which the lowest floor of a house is suspended above the ground on continuous foundation walls.

Cribbing – Temporary supports usually consisting of layers of heavy timber

Datum plane – See "Elevation datum plane."

Debris – Materials carried by floodwaters, including objects of various sizes and suspended soils.

Design capacity – Volume of water that a channel, pipe, or other drainage line is designed to convey.

Dry floodproofing – Protecting a building by sealing its exterior walls to prevent the entry of flood waters.

Elevation – In retrofitting, the process of raising a house or other building so that it is above the height of a given flood.

Elevation datum plane – Arbitrary surface that serves as a common reference for the elevations of points above or below it. Elevations are expressed in terms of feet, meters, or other units of measure and are identified as negative or positive depending on whether they are above or below the datum plane.

Erosion – Process by which flood waters lower the ground surface in an area by removing upper layers of soil.

Federal Emergency Management Agency (FEMA) – Independent agency created in 1978 to provide a single point of accountability for all Federal activities related to disaster mitigation and emergency preparedness, response, and recovery. FEMA administers the NFIP.

Federal Insurance Administration (FIA) – Component of FEMA directly responsible for administering the flood insurance aspects of the NFIP.

Fill – Material such as soil, gravel, or stone which is dumped in an area and to increase the ground elevation. Fill is usually placed in layers and each layer compacted (see "Compaction").

Flap valve – see "Check valve."

Flash flood – Flood that rises very quickly and usually is characterized by high flow velocities. Flash floods often result from intense rainfall over a small area, usually in areas of steep terrain.

Flood – Under the NFIP, a partial or complete inundation of normally dry land areas from 1) the overland flow of a lake, river, stream, ditch, etc., 2) the unusual and rapid accumulation or runoff of surface waters; and 3) mudflows or the sudden collapse of shoreline land.

Flood depth – Height of flood waters above the surface of the ground at a given point.

Flood duration – Amount of time between the initial rise of flood, including freeboard, waters and their recession.

Flood elevation – Height of flood waters above an elevation datum plane.

Flood frequency – Probability, expressed as a percentage, that a flood of a given size will be equaled or exceeded in any given year. The flood that has a 1-percent probability (1 in 100) of being equaled or exceeded in any given year is often referred to as the 100-year flood. Similarly, the floods that have a 2-percent probability (1 in 50) and a 0.2-percent (1 in 500) of being equaled or exceeded in any year are referred to as the 50-year flood and the 500-year flood, respectively.

Flood Protection Elevation (FPE) – Elevation of the highest flood, including freeboard, that a retrofitting method is intended to protect against.

Floodplain – Any area susceptible to inundation by water from any source. See "Regulatory floodplain."

Floodplain management – Program of corrective and preventive measures for reducing flood damage, including flood control projects, floodplain land use regulations, floodproofing or retrofitting of buildings, and emergency preparedness plans.

Floodproofing – Structural or nonstructural changes or adjustments included in the design, construction, or alteration of a building that reduce damage to the building and its contents from flooding and erosion. See "Dry floodproofing" and "Wet floodproofing."

Floodwall – Flood barrier constructed of manmade materials, such as concrete or masonry.

Floodway – Portion of the regulatory floodplain that must be kept free of development so that flood elevations will not increase beyond a set limit – a maximum of 1 foot under the National Flood Insurance Program (NFIP). The floodway usually consists of the stream channel and land along its sides.

Flow velocity – Speed at which water moves during a flood. Velocities usually vary across the floodplain. They are usually greatest near the channel and lowest near the edges of the floodplain.

Footing – Enlarged base of a foundation wall or independent vertical member (such as a pier, post, or column) for a house or other structure, including a floodwall. A footing provides support by spreading the load of a structure so that the bearing capacity of the soil is not exceeded.

Freeboard – Additional amount of height incorporated into the FPE to account for uncertainties in the determination of flood elevations.

Frequency – See "Flood frequency."

Grade beam – In a slab foundation, a support member cast as an integral part of the slab, as opposed to a separate footing.

Hazard mitigation – Action taken to reduce or eliminate long-term risk to people and property from hazards such as floods, earthquakes, and fires.

Human intervention – Any action that a person must take to enable a flood protection measure to function as intended. This action must be taken every time flooding threatens.

Hydrodynamic force – Force exerted by moving water.

Hydrostatic force – Force exerted by water at rest, including lateral pressure on walls and uplift (buoyancy) on floors.

Impervious soils – Soils that resist penetration by water.

Levee – Flood barrier constructed of compacted soil.

Local officials – Community employees who are responsible for floodplain management, zoning, permitting, building code enforcement, and building inspection.

Lowest Adjacent Grade (LAG) – Elevation of the lowest ground surface that touches any of the exterior walls of a building.

Lowest floor – Floor of the lowest enclosed area within the building, including the basement.

Masonry veneer – Nonstructural, decorative, exterior layer of brick, stone, or concrete block added to the walls of a building.

Mean Sea Level (MSL) – Datum plane; the average height of the sea for all stages of the tide, usually determined from hourly height observations over a 19-year period on an open coast or in adjacent waters having free access to the sea.

National Geodetic Vertical Datum (NGVD) – Elevation datum plane previously used by FEMA for the determination of flood elevations.

North American Vertical Datum Plane – Elevation datum currently used by FEMA for the determination of flood elevations.

Passive retrofitting method – Method that operates automatically, without human intervention. See "Active retrofitting method."

Permeable Soils – Soils that water can easily penetrate and spread through.

Pier – Vertical support member of masonry or cast-in-place concrete that is designed and constructed to function as an independent structural element in supporting and transmitting both building loads and environmental loads to the ground.

Piling – Vertical support member of wood, steel, or precast concrete that is driven or jetted into the ground and supported primarily by friction between the pilings and the surrounding earth. Piling often cannot act as independent support units and therefore are often braced with connections to other pilings.

Post – Long vertical support member of wood or steel set in holes that are backfilled with compacted material. Posts often cannot act as independent support units and therefore are often braced with connections to other posts.

Precast concrete – Concrete structures and structural members brought to the construction site in completed form.

Rates of rise and fall – How rapidly the elevation of the water rises and falls during a flood.

Regulatory floodplain – Flood hazard area within which a community regulates development, including new construction, the repair of substantially damaged buildings, and substantial improvements to existing buildings. In communities participating in the NFIP, the regulatory floodplain must include at least the area inundated by the base flood, also referred to as the Special Flood Hazard Area (SFHA). See "Floodplain."

Reinforcement – Inclusion of steel bars in concrete members and structures to increase their strength.

Relocation – In retrofitting, the process of moving a house or other building to a new location outside the flood hazard area.

Retrofitting – Making changes to an existing house or other building to protect it from flooding or other hazards.

Riprap – Pieces of rock added to the surface of a fill slope, such as the side of a levee, to prevent erosion.

Saturated soils – Soils that have absorbed, to the maximum extent possible, water from rainfall or snowmelt.

Scour – Process by which flood waters remove soil around objects that obstruct flow, such as the foundation walls of a house.

Sealant – In retrofitting, a waterproofing material or substance used to prevent the infiltration of flood water.

Service equipment – In retrofitting, the utility systems, heating and cooling systems, and large appliances in a house.

Slab-on-grade – Type of foundation in which the lowest floor of the house is formed by a concrete slab that sits directly on the ground. The slab may be supported by independent footings or integral grade beams.

Special Flood Hazard Area (SFHA) – Portion of the floodplain subject to inundation by the base flood, designated Zone A, AE, A1 - A30, AH, AO, V, VE, V1 - V30, or M on a FIRM.

Storm surge – Rise in the level of the ocean that results from the decrease in atmospheric pressure associated with hurricanes and other storms.

Subgrade – Below the level of the ground surface.

Substantial damage – Damage of any origin sustained by a structure whereby the cost of restoring the structure to its before damaged condition would equal or exceed 50 percent of the market value of the structure before the damage occurred.

Substantial improvement – Any reconstruction, rehabilitation, addition, or other improvement of a structure, the cost of which equals or exceeds 50 percent of the market value of the structure before the start of construction of the improvement. This term applies to structures that have incurred substantial damage, regardless of the actual repair work performed.

Sump pump – Device used to remove water from seepage or rainfall that collects in areas protected by a levee, floodwall, or dry floodproofing. In addition, a sump pump is often part of a standard house drainage system that removes water that collects below a basement slab floor.

Tsunami – Great sea wave produced by an undersea earth movement or volcanic eruption.

Veneer – See "Masonry veneer."

Walkout-on-grade basement – Basement whose floor is at ground level on at least one side of a house. The term "walkout" is used because most basements of this type have an outside door at ground level. A walkout-on-grade basement is not considered a basement under the NFIP. See "Basement".

Wet floodproofing – Protecting a building by allowing flood waters to enter so that internal and external hydrostatic pressures are equalized. Usually, only enclosed areas used for parking, storage, or building access are wet floodproofed.

Appendix C

FEMA Offices

The addresses and telephone numbers of the 10 FEMA Regional Offices are listed below. Staff members of the Regional Office for your area can give you more information about retrofitting, hazard mitigation, and the National Flood Insurance Program.

FEMA HEADQUARTERS
Office of the Associate Director for Mitigation
500 C Street, SW.
Washington, DC 20472
(202) 646-4622

REGION I – CT, ME, NH, RI, VT
J. W. McCormack POCH, Room 462
Boston, MA 02109-4595
(617) 223-9561

REGION II – NJ, NY, PR, VI
26 Federal Plaza, Room 1337
New York, NY 10278-0002
(212) 225-7203

REGION III – DE, DC, MD, PA, VA, WV
Liberty Square Building, Second Floor
105 S. Seventh Street
Philadelphia, PA 19106-3316
(215) 931-5750

REGION IV – AL, FL, GA, KY, MS, NC, SC, TN
Koger Center – Rutgers Building
3003 Chamblee-Tucker Road
Atlanta, GA 30341
(770) 220-5400

REGION V – IL, IN, MI, MN, OH, WI
175 West Jackson Boulevard, Fourth Floor
Chicago, IL 60604-2698
(312) 408-5548

REGION VI – AR, LA, NM, OK, TX
Federal Regional Center
800 North Loop 288
Denton, TX 76201-3698
(940) 898-5127

REGION VII – IA, KS, MO, NE
2323 Grand Boulevard, Suite 900
Kansas City, MO 64108-2670
(816) 283-7002

REGION VIII – CO, MT, ND, SD, UT, WY
Denver Federal Center, Building 710
P.O. Box 25267
Denver, CO 80255-0267
(303) 235-4830

REGION IX – AZ, CA, HI, NV
Presidio of San Francisco
P.O. Box 29998
San Francisco, CA 94129-1250
(415) 923-7177

REGION X – AK, ID, OR, WA
Federal Regional Center
130 228th Street, SW.
Bothell, WA 98021-9796
(425) 487-4678

To order copies of Flood Insurance Rate Maps, and for information about Flood Insurance Study reports, call the FEMA Map Service Center toll-free at 1-800-358-9616, or mail a Flood Insurance Map Order Form (available from the Service Center) to the following address:

Federal Emergency Management Agency
Mitigation Directorate – Map Service Center
6730 Santa Barbara Court
Baltimore, MD 20221-5624

Appendix D

NFIP State Coordinating Agencies

ALABAMA
Alabama Emergency Management Agency
The State House, Suite 127
P.O. Box 301701
Montgomery, AL 36130-1701
(334) 353-5716

ALASKA
Alaska Department of Community and Regional Affairs
Municipal and Regional Assistance Division
333 W. 4th Avenue, Suite 220
Anchorage, AK 99501-2341
(907) 269-4500

ARIZONA
Arizona Department of Water Resources
500 N. Third Street, 2nd Floor
Phoenix, AZ 85004-3903
(602) 417-2400

ARKANSAS
Arkansas Soil and Water Conservation Commission
101 E. Capitol, Suite 350
Little Rock, AR 72201-3823
(501) 682-3969

CALIFORNIA
California Department of Water Resources
Division of Flood Management
1416 9th Street, Room 1623
Sacramento, CA 95814
(916) 653-9902

COLORADO
Colorado Water Conservation Board
State Centennial Building, Room 721
1313 Sherman Street
Denver, CO 80203
(303) 866-3441

CONNECTICUT
State Department of Environmental Protection
168 Capitol Avenue, Room 207
Hartford, CT 06106
(203) 566-7244

DELAWARE
Department of Natural Resources and Environmental Control
Division of Soil and Water Conservation
99 Kings Highway
P.O. Box 1401
Dover, DE 19903
(302) 739-4411

DISTRICT OF COLUMBIA
Department of Consumer and Regulatory Affairs
614 H Street, NW., Suite 500
Washington, DC 20001
(202) 727-7577

FLORIDA
Department of Community Affairs
William E. Sadowski Building
2555 Shumard Oak Boulevard
Tallahassee, Florida 32399
(904) 413-9960

GEORGIA

Department of Natural Resources
Environmental Protection Division
7 Martin Luther king, Jr., Drive, SW.
Atlanta, GA 30334
(404) 656-6382

GUAM (011) 671-477-9841
Guam Department of Public Works
Post Office Box 2877
Agana, Guam 96910
(011) 671-477-7567

HAWAII
Hawaii Board of Land and Natural Resources
P.O. Box 373
Honolulu, HI 96809
(808) 587-0222

IDAHO
Department of Water Resources
State House
1301 N. Orchard
Boise, ID 83720
(208) 327-7993

ILLINOIS
Illinois Department of Natural Resources
Office of Water Resources
524 South Second Street
Springfield, IL 62701-1787
(217) 782-3862

INDIANA
Indiana Department of Natural Resources
402 W. Washington Street, Room W264
Indianapolis, IN 46204-2743
(317) 232-4178

IOWA
Iowa Department of Natural Resources
Wallace State Office Building
Des Moines, IA 50319
(515) 281-8942

KANSAS
Kansas Division of Water Resources
901 S. Kansas, 2nd Floor
Topeka, KS 66612-1283
(785) 296-2933

KENTUCKY
Kentucky Department of Natural Resources
Division of Water
Frankfort Office Park
14 Reilly Road
Frankfort, KY 40601
(502) 564-3410

LOUISIANA
Louisiana Department of Transportation and Development
Office of Public Works
Floodplain Management Section
P.O. Box 94245
Baton Rouge, LA 70804-9245
(504) 379-1432

MAINE
Maine State Planning Office
38 State House Station
184 State Street
Augusta, ME 04333-0038
(207) 289-8050

MARYLAND
Maryland Water Resources Administration
Tawes State Office, Building E-2
580 Taylor Avenue
Annapolis, MD 21401
(301) 974-3825

MASSACHUSETTS
Massachusetts Division of Water Resources
Salltonstall Building, Room 1304
100 Cambridge Street
Boston, MA 02202
(617) 727-3267

MICHIGAN
Michigan Land and Water Management Division
Department of Environmental Quality
P.O. Box 30458
Lansing, MI 48909-7958
(517) 335-3182

MINNESOTA
Flood Plains/Shoreline Management Section
Division of Waters
Department of Natural Resources
500 LaFayette Road, Box 32
St. Paul, MN 55515-4032
(612) 296-9226

MISSISSIPPI
Mississippi Emergency Management Agency
1410 Riverside Drive
P.O. Box 4501
Jackson, MS 39216
(602) 960-9031

MISSOURI
Missouri Emergency Management Agency
P.O. Box 116
Jefferson City, MO 65102
(573) 526-9141

MONTANA
Montana Department of Natural Resources and Conservation
1520 East 6th Avenue
Helena, MT 59620-2301
(406) 444-6646

NEBRASKA
Nebraska Natural Resources Commission
301 Centennial Mall South
P.O. Box 94876
Lincoln, NE 68509
(402) 471-2081

NEVADA
Nevada Division of Water Planning
1550 East College Parkway, Suite 142
Carson City, NV 89706-7921
(702) 687-3600

NEW HAMPSHIRE
Governor's Office of Emergency Management
State Office Park South
107 Pleasant Street
Concord, NH 03301
(603) 271-2231

NEW JERSEY
New Jersey Department of Environmental Protection
Division of Coastal Resources
CN 419
501 East State Street
Trenton, NJ 08619
(609) 292-2296

NEW MEXICO
New Mexico Emergency Management Bureau
P.O. Box 1628
Santa Fe, NM 87504-1628
(505) 827-9222

NEW YORK
New York Department of Environmental Conservation
Flood Protection Bureau
50 Wolf Road, Room 330
Albany, NY 12233-3507
(518) 457-3157

NORTH CAROLINA
North Carolina Department of Crime Control and Public Safety
Division of Emergency Management
116 West Jones Street
Raleigh, NC 27603-1335
(919) 733-3427

NORTH DAKOTA
North Dakota State Water Commission
900 East Boulevard
Bismark, ND 58505
(701) 224-2750

OHIO
Ohio Department of Natural Resources
Division of Water
Flood Plain Management
1939 Fountain Square, Building E-3
Columbus, OH 43224
(614) 265-6750

OKLAHOMA
Oklahoma Water Resources Board
600 N. Harvey
Oklahoma City, OK 73101
(405) 231-6750

OREGON
Department of Land Conservation Development
1175 Court Street, NE.
Salem, OR 97310
(503) 378-2332

PENNSYLVANIA
Pennsylvania Department of Community and Economic Development
Forum Building, Room 318
Harrisburg, PA 17120
(717) 787-7402

PUERTO RICO
Puerto Rico Planning Board
P.O. Box 41119, Minillas Station
De Diego Avenue, Stop 22
San Juan, PR 00940-90985
(809) 727-4444

RHODE ISLAND
Rhode Island Department of Administration
Statewide Planning Program
1 Capitol Hill
Providence, RI 02908-5872
(401) 277-6478

SOUTH CAROLINA
South Carolina Department of Natural Resources
Flood Mitigation Program
2221 Devine Street, Suite 222
Columbia, SC 29205
(803) 734-9103

SOUTH DAKOTA
South Dakota Disaster Assistance Programs
Emergency and Disaster Services
500 East Capitol
Pierre, SD 57501
(605) 773-3231

TENNESSEE
Tennessee Department of Economic and Community Development
Division of Community Development
320 Sixth Avenue, North
Sixth floor
Nashville, TN 37219-5408
(615) 741-2211

TEXAS
Texas Natural Resources Conservation Commission
Capitol Station
P.O. Box 13087
Austin, TX 78711-3087
(512) 239-4771

UTAH
Utah Department of Public Safety
Division of Comprehensive Emergency Management
450 N. Main
Salt Lake City, UT 84114
(801) 538-3400

VERMONT
Vermont Division of Water Resources
Agency of Environmental Conservation
10 North Building
103 South Main Street
Waterbury, VT 05676
(802) 244-6951

VIRGIN ISLANDS
Department of Planning and Natural Resources
Charlotte Amailie – Nisky Center, Suite 231
St. Thomas, VI 00802
(809) 774-3320

VIRGINIA
Virginia Department of Conservation and Historic Resources
Division of Soil and Water Conservation
203 Governor Street, Suite 206
Richmond, VA 23219
(804) 371-6136

WASHINGTON
Washington Department of Ecology
P.O. Box 47690
Olympia, WA 98504
(206) 459-6791

WEST VIRGINIA
West Virginia Office of Emergency Services
Room EB-80
Capitol Building
Charleston, WV 25305
(304) 348-5380

WISCONSIN
Wisconsin Department of Natural Resources
Floodplain - Shoreland Management Section
P.O. Box 7921
Madison, WI 53707
(608) 266-1926

WYOMING
Wyoming Emergency Management Agency
P.O. Box 1709
Cheyenne, WY 82003
(307) 777-4900

Appendix E

State Historic Preservation Offices

ALABAMA
Alabama Historical Commission
725 Monroe Street
Montgomery, AL 36130
(205) 242-3184

ALASKA
Alaska Department of Natural Resources
Office of History and Archeology
Division of Parks
P.O. Box 107001
Anchorage, AK 99510-7001
(907) 762-2622

ARIZONA
Arizona State Parks
800 West Washington
Suite 415
Phoenix, AZ 85007
(602) 542-4009

ARKANSAS
Arkansas Historic Preservation Program
The Heritage Center
225 East Markham
Suite 200
Little Rock, AR 72201
(501) 324-9346

CALIFORNIA
Office of Historic Preservation
Department of Parks & Recreation
P.O. Box 942896
Sacramento, CA 94296-9824
(916) 653-6624

COLORADO
Colorado Historical Society
1300 Broadway
Denver, CO 80203
(303) 866-2136

CONNECTICUT
Connecticut Historical Commission
59 South Prospect Street
Hartford, CT 06106
(203) 566-3005

DELAWARE
Division of Historical and Cultural Affairs
Hall of Records
P.O. Box 1401
Dover, DE 19901
(302) 739-5313

DISTRICT OF COLUMBIA
Department of Consumer and Regulatory Affairs
District Building
1350 Pennsylvania Avenue, NW.
Washington, DC 20004
(202) 727-6365

FLORIDA
Division of Historical Resources
Department of State
R. A. Gray Building
500 South Bronough Street
Tallahassee, FL 32399-0250
(904) 488-1480

GEORGIA
Office of Historical Preservation
205 Butler Street, SE.
1456 Floyd Towers East
Atlanta, GA 30334
(404) 656-2840

HAWAII
Department of Land and Natural Resources
P.O. Box 621
Honolulu, HI 96809
(808) 548-6550

IDAHO
Idaho State Historical Society
210 Main Street
Boise, ID 83702
(208) 334-2682

ILLINOIS
Illinois Historic Preservation Agency
1 Old State Capitol Plaza
Springfield, IL 62701-1512
(217) 785-9045

INDIANA
Department of Natural Resources
402 West Washington Street
Indiana Government Center South
Room C-256
Indianapolis, IN 46204
(317) 232-4020

IOWA
State Historical Society of Iowa
Capitol Complex
East 6th and Locust Streets
Des Moines, IA 50319
(515) 281-8837

KANSAS
Kansas State Historical Society
120 West 10th
Topeka, KS 66612
(913) 296-3251

KENTUCKY
Kentucky Heritage Council
300 Washington Street
Frankfort, KY 40601
(502) 564-7005

LOUISIANA
Office of Cultural Development
Department of Culture, Recreation and Tourism
P.O. Box 44247
Baton Rouge, LA 70804
(504) 342-8200

MAINE
Maine Historic Preservation Commission
55 Capitol Street
Station 65
Augusta, ME 04333
(207) 289-2132

MARYLAND
Department of Housing and Community
Development
100 Community Place, 3rd Floor
Crownsville, MD 21401
(410) 514-7662

MASSACHUSETTS
Massachusetts Historical Commission
80 Boylston Street
Suite 310
Boston, MA 02116
(617) 727-8470

MICHIGAN
Bureau of History
Department of State
717 West Allegan Street
Lansing, Michigan 49654
(517) 373-0511

MINNESOTA
Minnesota Historical Society
690 Cedar Street
St. Paul, MN 55101
(612) 296-2747

MISSISSIPPI
Mississippi Department of Archives and History
P.O. Box 571
Jackson, MS 39205-0571
(601) 359-6850

MISSOURI
State Department of Natural Resources
205 Jefferson
P.O. Box 176
Jefferson City, MO 65102
(314) 751-4422

MONTANA
State Historic Preservation Office
Montana Historical Society
225 North Roberts
Helena, MT 59620-9990
(406) 444-7715

NEBRASKA
Nebraska State Historical Society
P.O. Box 82554
Lincoln, NE 68501
(402) 471-4787

NEVADA
Division of Historic Preservation and Archeology
123 West Nye Lane
Room 208
Carson City, NV 89710
(702) 687-5138

NEW HAMPSHIRE
Division of Historical Resources
and State Historic Preservation Office
P.O. Box 2043
Concord, NH 03301
(603) 271-3483

NEW JERSEY
Department of Environmental Protection
501 East State Street
CN 402
Trenton, NJ 08625
(609) 292-2885

NEW MEXICO
Historic Preservation Division
Office of Cultural Affairs
Villa Rivera
228 East Palace Avenue
Santa Fe, NM 87503
(505) 827-6320

NEW YORK
Parks, Recreation and Historic Preservation
Agency Building 1
Empire State Plaza
Albany, NY 12238
(518) 474-0443

NORTH CAROLINA
Division of Archives and History
Department of Cultural Resources
109 East Jones Street
Raleigh, NC 27601-2807
(919) 733-7305

NORTH DAKOTA
State Historical Society of North Dakota
Heritage Center
612 East Boulevard Avenue
Bismarck, ND 58505
(701) 224-2667

OHIO
Ohio Historical Society
Historic Preservation Division
1985 Velma Avenue
Columbus, OH 43211
(614) 297-2470

OKLAHOMA
Oklahoma Historical Society
2100 North Lincoln Boulevard
Oklahoma City, OK 73105
(405) 521-2491

OREGON
State Parks and Recreation Department
525 Trade Street, SE
Salem, OR 97310
(503) 378-5019

PENNSYLVANIA
Pennsylvania Historical and Museum
Commission
P.O. Box 1026
Harrisburg, PA 17108
(717) 787-2891

RHODE ISLAND
Rhode Island Historical Preservation
Commission
Old State House
150 Benefit Street
Providence, RI 02903
(401) 277-2678

SOUTH CAROLINA
Department of Archives and History
P.O. Box 11669
Columbia, SC 29211
(803) 734-8592

SOUTH DAKOTA
South Dakota State Historical Society
Cultural Heritage Center
900 Governors Drive
Pierre, SD 57501
(605) 773-3458

TENNESSEE
Department of Conservation
701 Broadway
Nashville, TN 37243-0442
(615) 742-6758

TEXAS
Texas Historical Commission
P.O. Box 12276, Capitol Station
Austin, TX 78711
(512) 463-6100

UTAH
Utah State Historical Society
300 Rio Grande
Salt Lake City, UT 84101
(801) 533-5755

VERMONT
Agency of Development and Community Affairs
109 State Street
Montpelier, VT 05609-0501
(802) 828-3211

VIRGINIA
Department of Historic Resources
Commonwealth of Virginia
221 Governor Street
Richmond, VA 23219
(804) 786-3143

WASHINGTON

Office of Archeology and Historic Preservation
111 West 21st Street
KL-11
Olympia, WA 98504
(206) 753-4011

WEST VIRGINIA

West Virginia Division of Culture and History
Historic Preservation Office
Cultural Center
1900 Kanawha Boulevard East
Charleston, WV 25305-0300
(304) 558-0220

WISCONSIN

Historic Preservation Division
State Historical Society of Wisconsin
816 State Street
Madison, WI 53706
(608) 264-6500

WYOMING

Wyoming State Historic Preservation Office
Barrett Building
2301 Central Avenue
4th Floor
Cheyenne, WY 82002
(307) 777-7013

AMERICAN SAMOA

Stan Sorensen, HPO
Department of Parks and Recreation
Government of American Samoa
Pago Pago, American Samoa 96799
011-684-699-9614

PUERTO RICO

Office of Historic Preservation
Box 82, La Fortaleza
San Juan, Puerto Rico 00901
809-721-2676

VIRGIN ISLANDS

Department of Planning and Natural
Resources
Nisky Center
45A Estate Nisky
Suite 231
St. Thomas, VI 00802
809-774-3320

Appendix F

Professional Organizations

The organizations listed below can provide information about registered design professionals and licensed contractors in or near the area where you live.

American Institute of Architects
1735 New York Avenue, NW.
Washington, DC 20090
(202) 626-7300

American Society of Civil Engineers (ASCE)
World Headquarters
1801 Alexander Bell Drive
Reston, VA 20191-4400
(703) 295-6300

International Association of Structural Movers (ISM)
P.O. Box 1213
Elbridge, NY 13060
(315) 689-9498

National Association of Home Builders
15th and M Street, NW.
Washington, DC 20090
(202) 822-0200

*U.S. Government Printing Office: 1998 — 621-539/93310